The Winegrowers' Handbook

A practical guide to setting up a vineyard and winery in the UK

Belinda Kemp & Emma Rice

First published in Great Britain 2012 by
Posthouse Publishing, The Old Post Office, Swanton Novers, Melton Constable, Norfolk, NR24 2AJ www.posthousepublishing.com

A CIP catalogue for this book is available from the British Library
ISBN 978 1 903872 28 4

A catalogue record for this book is available from the British Library.

Publisher: Rupert Wheeler
Editor: Catherine Charles

Printed in Great Britain

Authors Acknowledgements
We would like to thank the following people for their enthusiasm, co-operation, assistance and contributions to this book; The Urban Wine Company, Gerard and Jonica Fox from Hobdens Vineyard, Sarah Midgeley from Camel Valley Vineyard, Fred Langdale from Coates & Seely, Chris Carter from Langham Farm, Art Tukker, from Tinwood Estate, Mike Wagstaff from Greyfriars Vineyard, Simon Woodhead from Stopham Vineyard, Will Davenport from Davenport Wines, Victoria Ash from Hush Heath Vineyards, Stuart Barford from Bolney Estate, Kieron Atkinson from Renishaw Hall, Vineworks Ltd, Duncan McNeill from FAST Ltd, Alistair Nesbitt and Chris Foss from WineSkills, James and Gill Cummings from Panniers Farm, Janette Kelly from Meopham Valley Vineyard, Stephen Skelton MW, Matthew Bernstein of Kenton Vineyard, Peter Hall at Breaky Bottom, Bob Lindo at Camel Valley, Frazer Thompson at Chapel Down, Hambledon Vineyard Plc, Hattingley Valley Vineyard and Dermot Sugre at Wiston Estate.

Contents

Case Studies

Foreword

The current media interest and the success of English and Welsh wines have started many people thinking that they would like to get involved. There are a number of reasons for doing this, ranging from farmers seeking to diversify, to an investment, a lifestyle change, a retirement project, a serious commercial intent or just to fulfill a dream. Whichever is the driving force, this book is a starting point, but there are many considerations that should be ignored only at your peril.

Whatever your view on global warming and the ability of technology to provide solutions to all problems, when it comes to growing grapes you are dealing with a plant species that is not a native of these shores and you are thinking of growing it on the very upper edge of its accepted range. The British Isles do not have a continental climate to produce the long period of good light and warmth that grapevines need to provide ripe, healthy fruit for winemaking on a reliable year-on-year basis. The Atlantic influence and the northerly location combine to give a requirement for great care in choosing the location, the aspect, the soil type and the height above sea level for a place to grow grapes. It can be done – witness the success of those currently producing wines that please the writers, the professionals and the discerning wine-drinkers in the UK – but there is no guarantee of success with viable crops year after year.

You may wish to grow grapes and make the wine yourself for your own consumption - fine, but think about how much you and your family can actually drink! About a quarter of an acre is considered to be the maximum for a hobby and production for your family: as soon as you have more than this amount you will need to sell the wine or give it away. However, these courses of action will bring a lot of bureaucracy and cost into your world, due to customs and excise, licensing regulations, product liability, income tax and insurance - alcohol duty is payable on all bottles of wine sold or given away.

If this book has stimulated you to know more about the world of English and Welsh wines, the UK Vineyards Association (UKVA) is the organisation to which grape-growers and winemakers belong in order to receive and share information on grape-growing and winemaking. All who are interested in grape and wine production in the UK, large or small producers, and those who do not produce but who wish to be involved and informed, are welcome to join. Members will belong to the appropriate Regional Association which will provide contacts and organise local events, meetings and competitions.

I look forward to seeing your wine being put before the judges at the English & Welsh Wine of the Year Competition - the national competition for UK-produced wines from fresh grapes - which takes place each year in June. The wines are rigorously tasted to world-class standards by a team of Masters of Wine, and the awards are presented at a prestigious ceremony in July. Our aim is to help growers and winemakers have confidence that their wines can compete on quality with whatever the rest of the world sends to these shores, and ensure that there is a demand for our wines at prices that are realistic in relation to production costs. If you have a mind to getting involved with vines and wines in the UK, please contact the UKVA office: we will do all that we can to help.

Cheers!

Roger Marchbank
Deputy Chairman UKVA
July 2012

Introduction

It is commonly believed that the United Kingdom was introduced to winemaking by the Romans who invaded in 43 AD. Wrotham Pinot is descended from the original Roman vines, and is still grown at Fishbourne Roman Palace near Chichester, West Sussex. Wrotham Pinot gained its name in the 1950s when a grapevine was found growing on the wall of a cottage in Wrotham, Kent. Researchers discovered it was a natural Pinto Noir seedling descended from Roman grapevines, and it has now been shown that its DNA matches Pinto Noir. Archaeological surveys in Northamptonshire have revealed evidence that suggests vineyards were established during the Roman occupation there, as deposits of grapevine pollen were found dating from that time. Research has shown that grapevines were planted in 100 AD by the Romans at Bagden Farm, less than 350 yards from Denbies Estate, Surrey. However, the end of the Roman Empire brought a rapid decline in wine production.

The rise in popularity of wine in Europe started from 312 AD onwards, encouraged by Constantine when he made Christianity the Romans' official religion. Pope Gregory sent St Augustine to Britain in around 596 AD, to convert the people to the Roman version of Christianity, and it is believed that he transported wine with him. Thus European trading began. There could have been a small continuation of wine production in England at that time, but the next time wine production is recorded was in 731 AD when the Venerable Bede wrote in his Ecclesiastical History "wines are cultivated in several localities". However, it was not until around 950 AD, fifty years after King Alfred defeated the Vikings, that vineyards where thriving again in Somerset.

By the time of the Norman Conquest in 1066, grapevines were being grown for wine production in the grounds of monasteries across England, particularly in the south of the country. French monks were skilled winemakers, and came to England with William the Conqueror and his noblemen, who expected to drink wine with their meals. Mead and ale were also popular at this time. The Doomsday Book has approximately 40 vineyards listed, from East Anglia to Somerset. Most were in the south of England. Leeds Castle in Kent is listed as having a vineyard, as it still does today. A decline in winemaking began 200 years after the Norman Conquest, mainly due to the marriage of Henry II to Eleanor of Aquitaine in 1152. The marriage created a vast kingdom which included parts of France, resulting in the reduction of English wine production due to easy access to French wines. Not dissimilar to the situation today, these imported wines were competition for the more expensive home-produced wines. In the mid-13th century cooler summers affected grape-ripening, and in the mid-14th century the Black Death decreased the population, and grape-growing.

When King Henry VIII came to the throne in 1509 there were 139 vineyards in England and Wales, but the Dissolution of the Monasteries in 1536 impacted the country's wine production. Two hundred years later in England in 1703, the Methuen Treaty levied high duties on French wine, which led to the English becoming consumers of sweet fortified wines from Spain and Portugal, such as sherry and port. These fortified wines were popular because they survived the long sea journeys well, presumably because they were less likely to oxidise than unfortified wines. Nevertheless, there is evidence in the 17th, 18th and 19th centuries that some noblemen in England were growing grapes and producing wine.

King James I (1603–1625) had a vineyard in the now prestigious and expensive residential area of Oatlands Park, Weybridge, Surrey. In 1666, the gardener to Charles II, John Rose, planted vines in the garden at St James's Palace, and wrote an article on the cultivation of vines in this country. It was titled "The English Vineyard Vindicated", and included site selection, grape varieties, pruning, training and grapevine upkeep. Two thousand vines were planted by the Earl of Salisbury, Robert Cecil, and then, in 1738 the Hon Charles Hamilton planted vines in his garden at Painshill Park, Surrey, where there is still a vineyard today.

The Marquis of Bute planted a commercial-scale vineyard at Castell Coch, South Wales, and by the time he died in 1905 it consisted of 63,000 vines. The enthusiastic industrialist even sent his head gardener, Andrew Pettigrew, to France to learn about viticulture. Records show that the last respectable wines were produced there in 1911, and all winemaking stopped after the First World War.

In the mid-19th century, after Phylloxera and Powdery mildew destroyed vineyards, the government, led by Lord Palmerston, cut tax on imported wines by 83 per cent. Once again foreign wines were cheaper than home produced wines! During the First World War no commercial wine was made, but there may have been vines growing in gardens by amateur grape-growers. George Ordish planted vines in Wessex and the south of England in 1938. When he returned from Champagne to Kent he recognised the similarity of the two climates. He was a talented winemaker and his experiments with the vineyard showed that grapes could ripen in our climate. He wrote a book in 1953 called 'Wine Growing in England', which appeared in 1953, and two other books on viticulture. He died in 1990. Ordish had also been in contact with Ray Barrington Brock, and had visited his research station in Oxted. After the Second World War, Ray Barrington Brock, a research chemist, set up a research station in his Oxted garden and over 25 years investigated 600 grape varieties with the aim of finding suitable varieties for the UK. He acquired cuttings and vines from universities and viticultural research stations throughout Europe (including Hungary), as well as Russia and the United States. Brock bought Müller-Thurgau (then called Riesling Sylvaner) and Seyve Villard 5/276 (Seyval blanc) to the UK. He also built a winery where he carried out experimental winemaking using different yeasts and production techniques. He lived until 1999 to see the start of the surge in UK grape-growing, and died aged 91. Another influence on English grape-growing was Edward Hymans, who wrote garden books. He planted his own vineyard, and wrote a book about the history and practice of grapevine growing in England. He increased the public's consciousness of English and Welsh winemaking via his writing and broadcasting. His books were called "The Grape Vine in England" and "Vineyards in England". He worked together with Brock and also searched the country for old grape varieties, which is how he found the vine growing on a cottage wall in Wrotham. In 1950 an article appeared in the Daily Mirror called "A bottle of Maidstone '49", which praised the work of Brock and Hyams and ended with the words "perhaps ten years hence you'll be raising a glass of sparkling Canterbury in honour of the men who made an English wine industry possible". Some of Brock's sparkling wines were still in the cellar in his research station in the 1980s.

In 1951, Major General Sir Guy Salisbury-Jones planted a commercial vineyard at Hambledon, north of Portsmouth, Hampshire, and made the first English wine to be sold commercially since the First World War. The current owners grubbed up the vines in 2004 and planted Chardonnay, Pinto Noir and Pinot meunier for sparkling wine production. Two more vineyards were planted in the mid-1950s, Beaulieu Estate, Hampshire, and the Merrydown Wine Company in Sussex.

During the 1960-80s, more vineyards were planted, and by the late 1980s and early '90s there were over 400 vineyards in England. Most of these vineyards were small, some being less than one acre, others five acres in size. In the 1970s, early English wines tried to emulate the popular sweet German wines such as Liebfraumilch and Hock. There were also wines made by blending white and red sweet still wine, called cream wine. The first English producers to make a small volume of bottled fermented sparkling wine from Müller-Thurgau and Seyval blanc vines were Nigel (de Marsac) Godden at Pilton Manor, Somerset, who planted vines in 1966, and Graham Barrett at Felsted Vineyard, Essex, who planted vines in 1967. In 1970, Sir Guy Salisbury-Jones planted a further 1,000 Chardonnay vines and tested bottle-fermented sparkling wine production. Salisbury-Jones also grew easier varieties such as Pinot auxerrois and Pinot meunier, which were used as the sparkling base wine. Unfortunately high manufacturing costs combined with the extended maturation time required meant its production was not financially viable, so production was halted.

In 1987, bottle-fermented sparkling wine was released by Carr Taylor Vineyard, near Hastings, East Sussex. At this time Carr Taylor was the major bottle-fermented commercial sparkling wine producer in the UK. Karl-Heinz Johner, at Lamberhurst Vineyards, started to trial sparkling wine production with Chardonnay, Pinot blanc and Pinot auxerrois, all grown at New Hall Vineyards, Essex, by Piers Greenwood. In 1977, Stephen Skelton MW established vineyards at Tenterden in Kent (now Chapel Down Wines), and made all the wine there.

From 1988 to 1991 he was General Manager and winemaker at Lamberhurst Vineyards, at that time the largest winery in the UK. In 1989 the non-vintage bottle-fermented sparkling wine called Lamberhurst Brut was launched, after three years on lees, but was only ever produced in small quantities. In 1989, David Cowderoy at Rock Lodge, East Sussex, made a sparkling wine called "Rock Lodge Impresario", and in 1992 he was instrumental in setting up Chapel Down Wines. Bottle-fermented sparkling wines that were produced from Chardonnay, Pinto Noir and Pinot meunier started to be released from 1997-98. The production of sparkling wines from the classic varieties, Chardonnay, Pinto Noir and Pinot meunier, started in the mid-1980s when Christopher (Kit) Lindlar persuaded several vineyards to plant these varieties. Lindlar set up his own contract winery at Biddenden Vineyards in 1985, after being winemaker at Horam Manor, and also produced wines at his own property, High Weald Winery, Kent.

The Americans, Stuart and Sandy Moss, had a major influence on wine production in the UK when they decided to plant a vineyard at Nyetimber near Pulborough, West Sussex in 1988, having bought the 49-ha estate in 1986. They were Lindlar's clients, and Lindlar supplied all the vines for vineyard between 1988 and 1991. Nyetimber's first award-winning commercial vintage was produced at Lindlar's High Weald Winery in 1992, with advice from consultant Jean-Manuel Jacquinot. Nyetimber's success both in wine competitions and commercially no doubt increased vineyard plantings of the three classic Champagne varieties in the UK. Nyetimber Ltd continues to expand and flourish under the new owner, Eric Hereema. Another award-winning vineyard, Camel Valley, Cornwall, owned by Bob and Annie Lindo, was established in 1989 with an initial planting of 8000 vines, and their son Sam is now the winemaker. Ridgeview Estate was established by Mike Roberts in 1995, a few years after the first vine plantings at Nyetimber, to concentrate on bottle-fermented sparkling wine production at Ditchling, East Sussex. Ridgeview Estate planted 13 clones of Chardonnay, Pinto Noir and Pinot meunier, a winery with underground cellar storage was built and the equipment came from High Weald Winery, which by now Lindlar had closed. At first, Ridgeview bought Chardonnay and Pinto Noir grapes from growers, and the first release was the 1996 Cuveé Merret Bloomsbury. Ridgeview Estate now produces a range of award-winning wines with names such as Belgravia, Bloomsbury, Cavendish, Fitzrovia, Grosvenor, Knightsbridge and Pimlico.

Due to the success of these vineyards, grapevine plantings have rapidly increased in the UK in the last decade. At a European sparkling wine competition in 2004, most of the top ten positions were taken by English wines, with French Champagnes taking the other places. English still wines have also started to win awards at major wine competitions, such as Decanter and the IWSC. There are now around 400 vineyards planted in the South East, South West, the Midlands, the North of England, Wales, and even one in Scotland. The majority of vineyards are in the south of England. Some of them sell their grapes to the major producers; many others are relatively small in size. Currently only 1 per cent of wine consumed in the UK is produced in the UK, with the rest being imported from abroad. As larger volumes are being produced it is hoped that more people will support and consume locally produced wines. Unfortunately, there remains confusion with the general public with terms "English" and "British" wine. "English" wine can only be made from grapes that have been grown in England, and the wine has to be produced in England. "British" wine, by contrast, is not made from grapes grown in England, but is produced from imported grape concentrate. "British" wines are low cost and at the bottom of the wine market in the UK.

While sparkling wine production continues to increase in the UK i.e. the planting of Rathfinny Estate, East Sussex, other producers continue extremely successfully with existing varieties such as Bacchus. There are also vineyards experimenting with different wine styles, such as Bolney Estate with sparkling red wine, Eglantine Vineyard with dessert wine, and Strawberry Hill with fortified wine made in the style of port. Some farms are planting vineyards to sell grapes to wineries, garden vineyards are growing in popularity, and UK wines are becoming internationally recognised. Therefore, this book has been written as a guide to those thinking or planning on setting up a vineyard or winery in the UK, and deals with all the issues that need to be considered.

Chapter One

Home winemaking and formal training

Case Studies

Home Winemaking and formal training

The planting of wine grapevines in gardens is growing in popularity in the UK. These garden vineyards are classified as hobby vineyards so must be registered on the United Kingdom Vineyard Register, which is the responsibility of the Food Standards Agency, specifically the Wine Standards branch. The wine regulations state that the information that must be provided to the Wine Standards branch includes the size of the vineyard and the number of different grapevine varieties planted. This information must be provided within six months of planting the vineyard or warning notices and fines can be imposed. This is part of the Statutory Instrument (SI 2011/2936), "The Wine Regulations 2011", which came into force on 30th December 2011. This gives the UK a legal standing to the many changes that came about through the European Wine Reform Process. All annual harvest and production declarations are part of the Vineyard Register, with the total production information being reported to the European Commission.

To register your garden as a vineyard and join the existing seventy vineyards classified as hobby vineyards, contact your local Wine Standards Officer via the Food Standards Agency website or download the documents from **www.food.gov.uk/aboutus/publications/winestandardsresources/**. Regarding home winemaking from garden grapevines, the law in Britain states that people may produce wine, but must not sell it. 0.5 acre/0.2 hectares is the maximum for a hobby vineyard and planting more means that the wine will need to be sold or given away. Giving away or selling the wine means becoming involved in customs and excise, licensing regulations, product liability, income tax and insurance. Additionally, duty must be paid on wine that is sold or given away. For details regarding UK wine schemes and varietal regulations of the English Wine - Protected Designation of Origin (PDO) and English Regional Wine - Protected Geographical Indication (PGI) schemes for England and Wales visit the

UKVA website **www.ukva.org.uk**. The DEFRA website also has full details of wine schemes including permitted grape varieties for PDO and PGI wines **www.defra.gov.uk/food-farm/food/protected-names/uk-registered-names/**. Further details regarding UK winemaking regulations are found in Chapter Four.

Many books and websites regarding home grape-growing and winemaking list varieties suitable for indoor and outdoor growing, but ultimately your choice of wine grape variety depends on local climate, soil and on the wine style you wish to make. Our advice is to grow recommended wine varieties that are already thriving in the UK. It is also useful to gain vineyard knowledge and hands-on experience prior to planting grapevines in your garden (*see* Training section) or making any type of investment. Local vineyards are a good place to volunteer for seasonal work to gain practical experience, and educational courses are available at Plumpton and Shuttleworth colleges.

The garden vineyard

Grapevines can be trained on garden fences, walls, arches, pergolas or trellis systems but need deep, free-draining soil: we recommend up to 100m above sea level in the UK and south facing. They should be sheltered from the wind as much as possible and planted where they can get plenty of sunlight to ripen the grapes properly. The soil nutrient status should be checked first to prevent excessive or low nutrient levels. Grapevines should be planted away from other fruit or vegetables that could harbour pests, such as lettuces which attract Light Brown Apple Moths. Phosphate levels are particularly important for root growth and any soil additions required such as fertiliser, compost or manure should be carried out prior to planting. Phosphorous levels in soils for UK wine grapevines should be 50ppm, potassium levels should be 200ppm, magnesium 110ppm and the potassium to magnesium ratio (K:Mg) should be 2:1 while the pH of soil should be 6.5. Nutrient-deficient soils can take a minimum of three years to correct. Therefore, it is advisable to purchase a home soil-testing kit with reagents included, from a garden centre or nursery, to test pH, nitrogen (N), phosphorous (P) and potassium (K). If planting grapevines in more than one area of the garden then all sites should be tested, as soil's pH can be different in one area of the garden to another. Some home grape-growers may not think it is important to test soil nutrients prior to planting grapevines in a back garden because plants are already growing successfully. However, it is essential to have the right balance of nutrients for vine establishment, vine growth, and yield, and to produce quality grapes for wine production.

Grapevine suppliers can be found on the United Kingdom Vineyard Association (UKVA) website **www.ukva.org.uk**, but limited information regarding clones and rootstock combinations, and their suitability to UK soils and weather, is currently available (*see* Chapter Two). To purchase small quantities of grapevines it may be easier to visit a local nursery or the RHS Gardens, Wisley, Surrey. Advice can be sought from the grapevine suppliers, local vineyards with similar soils, Vineyard Consultants, Vineyard Managers and the UKVA membership contact email list which is available to all vineyard and winery members who register with them. There is no rule stating that garden grapevines should be planted using rootstocks instead of on their own roots or from cuttings, but it is advisable in order to reduce the risk of phylloxera and its spread throughout the UK. Phylloxera devastated wine grape vineyards across Europe in the 19th Century, especially French vineyards. Phylloxera is native to North America, and its native grape species are partly resistant, but *Vitis vinifera* wine grapevines are extremely susceptible to it. For this reason it is advisable to plant *Vitis vinifera* varieties that are grafted on to American rootstocks. To reduce disease incidence, choose a grapevine that has been proven to be successful in the UK and that suits our climate, is an early ripening variety, is as disease resistant as possible, and that does not suffer from bunch compaction.

How to plant grapevines in your garden

There are many options available for training grapevines in the garden, but the aim should be to produce the best quality grapes to make your wine. To achieve this it is advisable to use proven training systems such as those found in commercial vineyards in the UK, like the Guyot system or the vertical shoot positioned system (VSP). Additionally the home grape-grower needs to consider the costs of establishing their garden vineyard and the amount of time required to manage the vines. Some training systems such as a Mosel Hertz seem aesthetically pleasing after pruning but can require considerable work to maintain fruit exposed to the sunlight during the growing season. Some training systems take more work than others, and the pruning style to be carried out will depend upon the training system used.

The best time to plant grapevines in a garden is early spring, and they can be planted so that they grow up against a wall, trellis or fence. Ensure grapevines are spaced approximately 1.2m–1.5m apart. The hole to be dug should be 15cm deep and 15cm away from the wall or fence. Ensure the grapevine is placed into the hole with the roots at the bottom, fill the hole with soil and secure it by firming the ground around it. Some gardeners place a mulch of compost or manure over the soil to shield roots from frost, and use tree guards to prevent pests i.e. rabbits from eating the new shoots. Some gardeners let three stems grow vertically in the first year by removing any shoots growing from the side. Allow the grapevines to become established before harvesting the grapes. Usually the rule is that the fruit can be harvested in the third year of grape production, but it is not uncommon for some vines to be harvested the second year after planting.

Growing grapes on a garden fence

If planting by a fence, a support is required and three or four support wires need to be installed. Mark the positions of the galvanised wires on the fence posts before drilling. A bolt should then be pushed through the bolt's hole and secured with a nut. Do not secure it too much because as the vines and grapes grow the wire tension will need to be altered. Wire should then be threaded through the bolt hole/eye, bent back, and twisted to hold it in place. The wire must then be pulled to the second post, cut and threaded through the bolt hole/eye, pulled, then twisted back to hold it secure.

Growing garden grapes in containers

Grapevines can also be planted in large pots. Clay ones are more stable as the vine grows bigger, and it can remain in them for several years. Potted grapevines need to have the top 15cm of compost removed every spring and a new layer of compost or manure added. They need regular watering and foliar feeding during the growing season to ensure they develop and grow appropriately. Grapevines grown in pots are often spur pruned and can be trained to one stem, a standard, with five or six branches at the top. In the first year of growth, remove all grapes and undesirable lateral shoots from the grapevine. The stem can be tied to a bamboo cane, and the stems that grow around the base should be removed.

Management of fence-grown grapevines

Pruning garden grapevines that grow against a wall or fence can cause confusion for garden grape-growers. Correct pruning should sustain a grapevine's ability to produce a good-quality crop, improve grapevine structure, expose grape bunches to sunlight, encourage the growth of next year's canes, and aid in diminishing the incidence of disease and pests (due to air circulation, and light and temperature increase in the fruit zone). The most important aspect of pruning is selecting the good-quality fruiting wood that must be retained on the grapevine and will hold grape bunches. Only minimal pruning of one-year-old shoots is needed, but selected trimming may be required to train the shape of the vine prior to the second year's growth starting. All lateral shoots and fruit that grow on the trunk should be removed. The permanent structure is the cordon that is on the top wire. During January to February (although some UK vineyards start pruning in December), each one-year-old shoot on the cordon should be pruned to either a three- or four-node spur (fruit spur) or a one-node renewal spur (vegetative spur). The spurs to be used as fruiting spurs should have the diameter size of a pencil. The vegetative spur produces vegetative shoots that are used for the following year's fruit spurs.

Keep garden grapevines free from weeds by hand weeding, or use mulch such as wood chips or plastic black sheets to suppress weed growth. Spring frost can cause trunk damage to young grapevines or kill the grapevine completely. There are several ways to prevent frost damage, including placing straw mulch around the base of the grapevine and covering the plant with plastic; and both can be removed when the weather improves.

Pests and diseases

While the UK is largely phylloxera-free there are many other pests and diseases that appear on grapevines, especially Botrytis bunch rot/grey mould produced by *Botrytis cinerea*, as well as powdery mildew (*Odium tuckeri*) and to a lesser extent downy mildew (*Peronospera viticola*). Garden grape-growers can use seaweed extract sprayed every two weeks during the growing season (except around flowering) to strengthen foliage. Wettable sulphur and Dithane or Mancozeb help to protect the vines against mildews. The "Bordeaux blend" of sulphur and copper has been used for many years, but it is important never to spray when flowering to ensure there is no disruption to pollination and fertilisation. Spray application times and recommended concentration rates must be strictly adhered to in order to prevent damage to the growth of the grapevines. Sprays can be purchased from garden centres and local nurseries, and the list of permitted sprays for the UK can be found on the UKVA website. Other grapevine diseases to be aware of in the UK, that have been found in European vineyards, include phomopsis cane and leaf spot, and the grapevine trunk disease *Botryosphaeria*, particularly the Diplodia seriata species (prev. *Botryosphaeria obtusa*). This particular species is the most widely spread of all trunk disease fungi in vines and other plants, but is relatively nonthreatening compared to some other trunk disease species. Another grapevine trunk disease to look out for is blackfoot disease (caused by *Cylindrocarpon fungus*). Chemical sprays are used in many wine regions throughout the world, and some are certified for use in organic viticulture.

Common vineyard pests in the UK include rabbits, deer, spider mites, beetles, grape berry moths, thrips, erineum mites, wasps, birds and vine weevils. Some pests, like deer, will not affect the garden grape-grower as much as commercial grape-growers, but protecting grapes from birds and wasp damage in the summer is of utmost importance. Identification of the disease or pest is paramount: learning about their life cycle and monitoring them will enable an informed decision regarding biological, cultural and chemical control options.

Purchasing grapes for home winemaking

Vineyards and wineries like to sell their grapes early in the year so while the garden grapevines are becoming established it may be useful to contact a local vineyard or winery to purchase a small volume of wine grapes to make your first home made wine. Some vineyards may prefer to sell larger quantities but others may be happy to sell smaller amounts or may know someone who has grapes to sell.

Home winemaking

There are several options available to garden grape growers and these include a) growing grapes to sell them, b) growing grapes under contract to a local winery, c) make the wine yourself from your grapes for your own consumption or d) grow grapes to have them made into wine under contract and the wine returned to you in bottle. If selling the home made wine then the wine is subject to duty and the details of the certification process and cost are contained on the UKVA website which includes labelling regulations **www.ukva.org.uk**. Alternatively garden grape growers can contact the Urban Wine Company cooperative and pool their grapes to make wine which is shared between all their members.

Home winemaking equipment

Home winemaking kits can be purchased which include the equipment, instructions and additives needed. For larger quantities of grapes it may be better to purchase equipment and additives separately. To produce up to 4.5 litres (6 bottles) of homemade quality wine you will need basic equipment including basic laboratory analysis apparatus. To monitor grape ripening pre-harvest a hydrometer and volumetric flask is required to analyse sugar levels/density, thermometer, a pH

Case study: The Urban Wine Company, London

The Urban Wine Company was set up in 2007 by Richard Sharp and some of his neighbours and friends who had grapevines in 'Furzedown', Tooting, South London. Richard was sitting in his garden enjoying a glass of wine and thought it was a shame that the grapes growing in his garden were going to waste. Richard is a Project Manager within Urban Regeneration and a freelance journalist and does not have a background in wine. His grape-growing is a hobby fitted around a full-time job and three young children. On holiday in France, Richard had seen villagers working together to bring in the grape harvest, and noted the camaraderie and common purpose bringing them together. He rounded up a group of friends, who pooled their grape crop and produced 20 bottles of "Chateau Tooting - Furzedown Blush". Richard's garden grapevine is an offshoot of his neighbour's vine that was planted more than 20 years ago from a pip from a supermarket bunch of grapes.

Richard used a community website to recruit other grape-growers, and enthusiasm for Urban Wine attracted new members from across London and beyond. The Urban Wine Company was championed in several articles - first local papers, then The Independent in November 2007 and an interview on the BBC news in 2009. Membership has grown each year and membership in 2011 had risen to just under 100 members.

The harvest date is estimated so as the majority of members' grapes are at their peak of ripeness. For the last few years, the collection has taken place in Tooting Common car park. A lorry is hired and members bring their plastic bags, buckets and crates of grapes to be weighed before they are driven to the winery. The Bolney Wine Estate in West Sussex, which offers winemaking for people growing grapes in their own gardens, produces the wine for The Urban Wine Company.

Members pay to join The Urban Wine Company - the annual fee for 2011 was £110. They do not pay for the grapes, but all members receive a share of the finished wine. Everyone receives six bottles, but those contributing more grapes are entitled to buy additional bottles in proportion to the amount of grapes contributed. The members may also name their own wine, and their bottles are labelled with their own bespoke label. The grapes must be disease-free, as one bunch with mildew will contaminate the entire container.

Members are given advice on how to grow healthy grapes. The Urban Wine Company provide Solaris (white), Rondo (red) or Phoenix (white) grapevines to new members. Producer members can bring any grape variety to harvest as long as the fruit is disease-free and clean. They have Pinot noir, Chardonnay, Muscadet, Tempranillo and Muller-Thurgau, but the majority are unidentified varieties.

The minimum contribution is 3kg of grapes, and they have many members with just one vine producing only 3kg of fruit. The largest grower is the Alexandra Allotment group in Epsom who contribute over 100kg of grapes. The Urban Wine Company is a collective for grape-growers, and the members meet up for harvest, the 'uncorking ceremony', and events through the year. In the future the hope is that urban wine production will spread to other cities and towns across England.

www.urbanwineco.com

meter (for juice and wine) and preferably titration equipment to measure acidity levels, and later sulphur dioxide levels (*see* Chapter Four).

For home winemaking some people use small crusher/destemming machines depending on whether white or red wine is being made. A 10 L bucket with lid and a 4.5 L plastic (or glass) demi-john and bung with a hole in it for a bubbler is needed. A siphon, a straining bag (for racking), a plastic funnel and Campden tablets which are sulphur-based tablets (potassium or sodium metabisulfite) . These are used predominantly in wine, cider and beer to kill bacteria, inhibit the growth of wild yeast and prevent oxidation of the wine. Bottling equipment including six bottles, corks, corking machine, shrink caps and labels may also be required for the finished wine.

The **www.lovebrewing.co.uk** website has full details of each of the ingredients in a Home Winemaking Kit and their importance and role in the winemaking process. Other home winemaking websites that offer advice and equipment include **www.homewinemaking.co.uk**, **www.hopshopuk.com**, **www.hopandgrape.co.uk**, **www.homebrew-shop.co.uk**, **www.homebrewit.co.uk**, **www.art-of-brewing.co.uk**, **www.brewgenie.co.uk**,**www.the-online-homebrew-companyco.uk**, **www.the-online-homebrew-company.co.uk**, **www.goodlifehome-brew.com and www.vigoltd.com**.

Additionally home brew and home wine shops are found in some UK towns and cities and are often listed in the local business directories and on community websites.

Home winemaking preparation

There are many winemaking recipes available for home winemaking as well as "ready to use" winemaking kits available from suppliers. Presented in this chapter is a modified method for small scale red wine vinification which is commonly used with replicates in wine research trials. This can be carried out using different size fermentation vessels i.e. 4.5 L, 10 L 30 L, according to the quantity of fruit but the same steps apply. Home winemakers tend to need six - seven kilos of grapes to produce five litres of finished wine and if you lack this amount then it can be supplemented with concentrated grape must or if you require more than your garden wine grapevines produce you may be able to source some from a local vineyard or winery.

Ensure all equipment is cleaned prior to picking the grapes as good sanitation is vital for successful winemaking to prevent spoilage. If it is the first time the equipment is to be used then hot water is sufficient but previously used equipment may benefit from a sulphur dioxide/citric acid based sanitiser available from home winemaking shops. Do not use chlorine, soap, detergent or perfumed based cleaners, as these are difficult to completely wash off and can affect the taste of your finished wine. Make sure gloves are worn when using and preparing sanitising solutions as they are caustic and can cause skin irritation.

Home winemaking recipe

The following text focuses primarily on a red winemaking technique for the home winemaker but further recipes for home white winemaking and fruit winemaking can be found at **www.wineworks.co.uk**.

The specific gravity on the hydrometer needs to be between 1078 and 1090 depending on the alcohol level required. 1090 will normally produce a wine with 13% alcohol by volume while 1078 will result in 11.5% alcohol by volume in the finished wine. This can be adjusted by adding grape concentrate or cane sugar prior to fermentation and Wine Standards branch figure is 16.5 g/l of sugar to produce 1% alcohol by volume although this is slightly low. Germany states 16.85 g/l, Australia states 16.95 g/l and France suggests 17 g/l will increase the alcohol by 1% by volume. The legal limit for alcohol increase in wine is 3% by volume by enrichment.

The grape bunches should be de-stemmed, crushed and the must, skins and seeds placed into 10 L buckets/fermentation vessels. These could be destemmed by hand for small volume of grapes, or a food processor with a tight lid could be used to crush the grapes. Alternatively after destemming the fruit and placing it into a bucket it could be crushed. Ensure the fermentation vessel is not filled to the top with grapes as this will result in overflowing during fermentation due to the carbon dioxide being produced by the yeast. Additionally make sure the room used for winemaking is well ventilated as carbon dioxide produced during fermentation is extremely dangerous.

Case study: Exton Park, Hampshire: Fred Langdale, Vineyard manager

Fred Langdale was travelling in New Zealand in 2001 and found a job in the prestigious 27-ha Peregrine Wines Vineyard in the Gibbston Valley, Central Otago, to earn money for his travels. He was put to work leaf-thinning, green harvesting and covering the rows of vines with bird netting, and it was this experience that ignited his interest in vineyard work. Upon his return in 2003, he enrolled on the Principles of Vinegrowing course at Plumpton College and attended lectures two days per week. The other three days he worked on the organic 8-ha Davenport Vineyard in Sussex. Fred assisted the Vineyard Manager in the vineyard as well as lending a hand in the winery with bottling, labelling, cleaning tanks, and cleaning the press. In 2004 Fred gained further experience by working in South Africa supervising a harvest team of sixty people and completing the winter pruning. The lure of the UK vineyards brought Fred back to Davenport Vineyards in 2005 as a full-time member of the vineyard crew. From 2006 to 2008 Fred supervised one of the Nyetimber Ltd vineyard sites in West Sussex, and since May 2008 has been employed as the Vineyard Manager at the 12-ha Exton Park Vineyard in Hampshire, producer of sparkling wine. **www.coatesandseely.com**

The temperature of the fermentation should be 19 - 28°C for red wine (lower temperatures are better for white wines). Pectinase can be added at this stage as this enzyme will help the must/juice to settle but is not always required in small red wine vinifications and is more common in white winemaking. If you are making 4.5 litres of white wine the must should be free of skins and seeds before being moved to a demi-john with bung and airlock (with water in the airlock). One hour after adding the pectinase the must can be inoculated with the yeast according to the manufacturer's instructions as it will need to be rehydrated first. Some home winemaking kits also have sachets of yeast nutrients. It is advisable to add these to prevent stuck fermentations occurring. While wild fermentations can be used in commercial winemaking it is not advised for young vines/grapes as they will lack naturally occurring yeast. Natural fermentations are carried out without the addition of *Saccharomyces cerevisae* cultured yeast but are prone to stuck fermentations that produce cabbage, onion and garlic smells. These can be difficult to restart in small vinifications so inoculation with commercially available wine yeast is advised.

Fermenting wines should be monitored twice daily for temperature and sugar levels/density by hydrometer. Fermentation temperatures for red wines should not exceed 30°C. The wine should ferment at a temperature between 19 - 27°C for red wines and 12 -15°C for white wines. For red wines it is important to extract colour, tannins and prevent stuck fermentations by punching down the cap that is formed from the skins and seeds. It is recommended for small vinifications that can finish quickly, punching down the cap two to three times per day using a wooden spoon or even a potato masher. Keep the fermenting vessel/bucket on a high surface that enables siphoning into a demi-john. Fermentation temperature is important because rapid fermentations will result in wines lacking flavour and aroma compounds. Therefore it is advisable to check them twice a day (especially small scale vinifications), ideally once in the morning and again in the evening.

Fermentation is complete when the hydrometer reads the same gravity reading for two days and will be in the range of 990 - 1000 and the cap of skins has submerged with the seeds at the bottom of the container. Larger volumes of wine should be pressed to extract more wine, colour and tannins from the grapes. This can be carried out using a small vertical hydraulic bladder and the wine should be pressed to 1.2 bars into demi-johns. Alternatively the wine can be poured into the demi-john using the siphon and plastic funnel to avoid loss of wine and the remaining skins and seeds can be pressed by hand or foot. Some English wines in many years require malolactic fermentation to convert the sour malic acid to softer lactic acid. Malolactic fermentation requires the addition of lactic acid bacteria (*Oenococcus oeni*) and will not proceed with high sulphur levels so campden tablets should not be added if malolactic fermentation is to be initiated. Wines need to be at 18°C for malolactic fermentation and can take 4 – 6 weeks for small vinifications. Following malolactic fermentation campden tablets should be added with subsequent further additions made periodically to maintain 20 ppm.

White wine needs clarifying to remove the cloudiness and ensure the wine is free from proteins. This can be done using fining agents from your home winemaking supplier and comes in sachets for small winemaking. Ensure the white wine is absolutely clear and this process usually takes 24 hours for 4.5 L demi-johns but can take up to 2 - 3 days. Some home winemakers adjust the acidity, sweetness and tannin levels at this stage but a commercial winemaker would do this prior to fermentation. Ideally wine should be filtered to remove particles and protect the wine from spoilage and small desktop filters are available to buy or use a straining bag with very small holes.

Oak barrel extract or chips can be added and stirred in to extract oak flavours and aromas during the ageing process then the wine can be bottled using cork or plastic tops. It is advisable and useful to keep records and a diary throughout the winemaking process to refer to the following year, with details of additions made to the wine and final volume produced.

Case study: Camel Valley Vineyards, Cornwall: Sarah Midgley, Assistant winemaker

Sarah Midgeley works as Assistant Winemaker at Camel Valley Vineyards, Nanstallon, near Bodmin, Cornwall. Sarah started working for Camel Valley during the summer of 2009, in the tasting room and vineyard. Camel Valley is owned by the Lindo family, Bob and Annie Lindo; their son, Sam, is the Winemaker. They produce a wide range of wines but are best known for sparkling wines.

Sarah initially did a BSc (Hons) in Biochemistry and Medical Biochemistry at the University of Manchester, and it was during this time that she became interested in wine. She did her WSET Level 2 and worked in a pub which specialised in wines from around the world. Having already completed an undergraduate degree, Sarah decided to take up the offer of a place on the one-year intensive Postgraduate Diploma in Viticulture and Oenology at Lincoln University, Canterbury, New Zealand.

Sarah gained her practical experience from working abroad and did summer contract vineyard work at Premium Viticulture, Marlborough, New Zealand in 2008. Sarah's first paid harvest was in 2009 at Tyrrell's Glenbawn Winery, Australia. There she gained practical winemaking experience, as the winery was run by a small team which meant she was able to perform a wide range of tasks and acquire laboratory experience.

In 2009 Sarah worked at William's Selyem Winery, California, for her second vintage and found it extremely useful from a formal training perspective. They dedicate several days at the start of harvest to training and safety briefings for their staff. In 2010 she worked at Kim Crawford Wines in Marlborough, New Zealand, operating and cleaning the nine presses, the crusher/destemmer, quality control and directing the flow of the juice from press to tanks. Further winemaking experience was gained at Tyrrell's Winery, Pokolbin, Hunter Valley, Australia in 2011. Due to a fairly small harvest from a difficult growing season, Sarah found she had less work than expected but was invited to help in the winery and laboratory at Cassegrain Wines, Port Macquarie, NSW, Australia.

www.camelvalley.com

Formal training

Part-time and full-time courses

Whether planting a commercial vineyard or a hobby vineyard it is essential to gain an understanding of grapevine biology and its annual growth cycle and management. For in-depth practical, and theory-based training in viticulture and oenology it is advisable to attend a specialised course. There are limited training options available in the UK, but there are viticulture and oenology undergraduate degrees available in Europe (although they are not taught in English). Some universities in Europe offer viticulture and oenology postgraduate degrees taught in English, but there are cost implications to consider. International viticulture and oenology training and degrees are taught in English in the United States of America, Australia, South Africa and New Zealand, but these have tuition fees, relocation expenses and visa requirements to consider.

The Wine and Spirits Education Trust (WSET) provides training for those who wish to enter the wine trade or are currently employed within it. Qualification levels and modules are based on the needs of wine trade and business employees, and include basic viticulture and oenology modules. **www.wset.co.uk**

The Institute of the Master of Wines (IMW) qualification is the wine industry's highest qualification and the Institute recommends that applicants hold the Wine and Spirit Education Trust Diploma, or another wine qualification of at least the same level (a bachelor or master's degree in oenology). Applicants are also required to have at least five years' professional experience within the wine industry. **www.mastersofwine.org**.

Additional information regarding garden grape-growing and home winemaking can sometimes be obtained from local wine circles that have members who are enthusiastic home winemakers. Attending wine tastings by local wine clubs, in wine shops or hotels, and visiting local wineries are invaluable ways to gain further understanding of grape-growing and winemaking in the UK.

Shuttleworth College, Bedfordshire is part of Bedford College and offers short part-time courses. These include subjects such as grape-

Case study: Langham Wine Ltd, Dorset: Chris Carter, Director of winemaking

In 2004, Chris Carter decided he wanted to write about wine, and went to an open day at Plumpton College. He ended up committing to a full-time HND in wine production (now a FdSc degree). He did work placements at Domaine de la Pertusaine, Maury, France; Chateau La Bouscade, in the Minervois region of the Languedoc-Roussillon; and a three-month internship at Clos du Val, Napa Valley, which was where he realised that making wine was what he really wanted to do.

Following graduation in 2006 Chris went to Spain with the idea of working a vintage there and learning Spanish to help him find employment in California. He found his way to the Priorat region, Catalunya where he worked the 2006 harvest at Alvaro Palacios Winery. He went to Australia in 2007 and worked at De Bortoli Winery, Yarra Valley. He subsequently received a phone call from Alvaro Palacios inviting him to work full time in Catalunya, and took up the offer, and stayed until February 2009 when the economic crisis hit Spain and half of the work force was laid off. Undeterred Chris moved to Mendoza, Argentina where he spent three months as a Winemaker at Bodega Benegas. Upon his return to Europe he began consulting for Langham Farms, who were at the time planning a new vineyard/winery in Dorset. Chris worked the 2009 harvest for David Leclapart in Trepail, Champagne before moving to Dorset to start work full time for Langham Farms. After two successful vintages in Dorset he is now Director of Winemaking for the newly incorporated Langham Wine Ltd, in charge of a 12-ha vineyard and a 15 tonne winery producing sparkling wine.

http://langhamwine.wordpress.com

vine varieties, vine preparation for planting, grapevine pruning and training, protection from pests and diseases, and winemaking theory and tasting. The College also provides training on the use of pesticides, and a variety of short courses on machinery use and maintenance. For further details contact:

Shuttleworth College, Tel 01767 626222
www.shuttleworth.ac.uk email enquiries@shuttleworth.ac.uk

Plumpton College, East Sussex. The College offers, in association with the University of Brighton, two-year Foundation Degrees and three-year Bachelor of Science Degrees in Wine Business and Production. These can be studied in full- or part-time modes and are specially designed for those wishing to enter careers in vinegrowing, winemaking and the wine trade, both in the UK and abroad. Students learn all about wine using the College's facilities; an 8-hectare vineyard and a Wine Centre containing laboratories, a wine-tasting room and a commercial winery. A range of other wine courses are available, including Foundation Diplomas in Wine Business and Production; The Wine Trade in Britain; Principles of Vinegrowing and Principles of Winemaking; Practical Wine Analysis; and one-day Wine Workshops. The Wine Department also delivers WSET (Wine and Spirits Education Trust) Level 2, 3 and 4 (Diploma) courses and is developing research facilities and provision for postgraduate degrees at Masters and PhD level. Tractor driving and pesticide courses are also available to students.

For further details of Plumpton College Tel 01273 890454
www.plumpton.ac.uk email enquiries@plumpton.ac.uk

WineSkills is a project managed by Plumpton College that organises workshops, master classes and a mentoring service for the UK wine-production industry. The one-day workshops cover subjects ranging from vine-pruning and pesticide application to winemaking issues such as bottling and quality control. The monthly master classes are delivered by specialists in their field, and the project facilitates visits to vineyard and wineries in the UK by consultants with international

Case study: Tinwood Estate, West Sussex: Art Tukker, Vineyard owner

The idea of owning a vineyard came to Art Tukker in his final year studying Agricultural Business Management at Wye College. For his final year dissertation he had to write about a farm diversification scheme so he visited Owen Elias, who was then Winemaker at Chapel Down Vineyard, Kent, who helped him with figures and ideas. Eventually, after making a full financial appraisal of the business, he became partners with Ridgeview Estate, East Sussex, who also helped in the beginning to source vines and other vineyard materials. They planted 11 hectares of vines on their farm in April 2007.

After six months Art moved to Marlborough, New Zealand, to do a vintage with Huia, a small (300 tonnes) high-quality business. He was part of a team of five who were expected to do everything in the vineyard.

After the vintage he returned to the UK in May and planted another 8ha of vines. At first the vineyard was being run alongside the other operations on the farm but, as the size and complexity of the operation increased, he decided to devote all his time to the vineyard. Art was doing all the tractor work and annual vineyard operations, as well as leading the vineyard team in constructing the trellis systems. In the same year he completed the week's intensive course at Plumpton College in both vinegrowing and winemaking. At the end of the year he helped Ridgeview with their harvest and subsequently in the winery.

Every year Art makes a point of travelling and spending time in another wine-growing region. In particular he returns to New Zealand to keep up to date with new ideas, practices and methods which he can take back with him to the UK. In 2012 his Vineyard Supervisor became his Vineyard Manager, after completing the Principles of Vinegrowing course at Plumpton College as a part time student over a year. Now after nearly five years of growing vines he finds he learns so much by just walking up and down his vineyard twice a week. Tinwood Brut 2009 was released two months ago and he is excited with the results of his hard work!

www.tinwoodestate.com

reputations. Further information can be obtained from the WineSkills website **www.wineskills.co.uk**, which also provides information on vinegrowing, winemaking and the wine business, plus a range of electronic resources including e-books and academic journals.

The Royal Agricultural College, Cirencester offers a Wine Business Management MBA **www.rac.ac.uk.**

Work experience at home and abroad

Most of the international Viticulture and Oenology two- and three-year courses include a work placement or vintage experience module. There are several vineyard and winery employment recruitment websites where international jobs are advertised. **www.winejobsonline.com** is New Zealand-based but often has jobs advertised around the world. The Australian vineyard and winery recruitment site **www.wineindustryjobs.com.au** and **www.vitijob.com** both advertise international vacancies. Additionally **www.winebusiness.com** advertises wine industry roles in USA. Many vineyards advertise employment opportunities on their websites and require application direct to the company. International vineyards and wineries often prefer applicants to have qualifications or previous experience, but enthusiastic students and individuals are often welcome. For European countries it is advised to contact them in their own language as it is more likely that you will receive a response, and you may need to speak the language of the country to work in some wineries. Applying direct to UK vineyards and Wineries or via the UKVA for either paid or voluntary work can be successful at the right time of year, prior to pruning or before summer canopy management work begins. Recently there has been an increase in wineries and vineyards using social media, and some employment vacancies are advertised on Facebook groups such as "Travelling Winemakers - Living the dream!!" **www.facebook.com/#!/groups/2883325456/**, or "The Cellarhand" **www.facebook.com/#!/pages/TheCellarhand/137238519717214**. Visa requirements, costs and the official paper work should be completed several months in advance because some visas require police and medical checks.

Chapter Two

Land and soil

Case Studies

Land and soil

UK commercial vineyards are divided into those that grow grapes but do not have winemaking facilities, and those that have wineries to make wine from their own fruit as well as from grapes processed under contract or purchased from contract vineyards. Most vineyards are situated in the South West (Cornwall, Devon, Dorset, Somerset, Gloucestershire) and South East of England (Hampshire, Surrey, Kent, Sussex and Wiltshire), with others in East Anglia and the Midlands, and some further north and in Wales. There has been a change in grape varieties in recent years, with an increase in the classic sparkling wine varieties, Chardonnay, Pinot noir and Pinot meunier, although there have been still wines made from other varieties, such as Pinot gris, Pinot noir and Bacchus, which have been well received. Annual production volumes fluctuate in the UK depending on weather conditions during the growing season. The total UK harvest in 2010 was 30,346 hectolitres, the highest recorded, and other large harvests occurred in 2006, 1996 and 1992. Further details regarding grape varieties by acreage can be found on the Food Standards Agency website **www.food.gov.uk/enforcement/sectorrules/winestandards/ukvineyards**.

When thinking about becoming a vineyard owner, it is important to consider practical issues such as availability of labour in the area and travelling distance to work, but the most important consideration is who the target market will be for the wines. Investigate your target market and whether there is a realistic market for your wine style/product and how your wine will be marketed to that sector. This information will ultimately determine your vineyard design details such as grape variety, training system and canopy management techniques. A detailed and thorough business plan should be written, to include the costs of vineyard establishment and equipment, and running the winery, and investigations should be made into competitors and marketing strategy.

Buying an existing vineyard

There are several land agents such as Strutt & Parker **www.struttand-parker.com**, Frank Knight **www.knightfrank.co.uk**, Turner Butler **www.turnerbutler.co.uk** and Carter Jonas **www.carterjonas.co.uk**, and dedicated websites such as **www.uklandandfarms.co.uk**, that occasionally advertise vineyards for sale, as well as land suitable for vineyard sites. The UKVA email list for existing members sometimes has details of vineyards that are available for purchase. There are also several stories across the country about new vineyard owners who approached a vineyard to see if it was for sale only to buy it several years later on the open market. There are advantages and disadvantages to buying an existing vineyard because, while the establishment has already taken place, the new owner inherits the existing grape varieties. The difficult work of planting, designing and establishing the vineyard has already been done. However, if the grape varieties planted are not suitable for the wine style the new owners want to produce, then the vineyard will need re-planting. Importantly any potential buyers must have access to the audited accounts of the vineyard. Potential sites/vineyards with agricultural buildings on them will improve the chances of getting planning permission for a winery or winery expansion. Additionally shelter/buildings for equipment such as tractors, sprayers or quad bikes is essential. The existing vineyard will also have an existing market for their wines, either locally or nationally. The vineyard purchaser also needs to consider accommodation, and whether there is a house on the land, although the majority of UK vineyards do have living accommodation. If the site does not have a house on it then the buyer must consider the practical implications of living away from the vineyard, including site security and travelling distance from home, especially during busy periods like harvest. The purchase of an existing vineyard means that the buyer inherits the grape varieties planted, vineyard design, the reputation of the wines and the current staff. This will be beneficial if the wine and its reputation is of high quality but can be challenging if the vineyard lacked expertise and the new buyer has to increase wine quality, manage a business, manage staff and improve sales. Thorough background research into the business, its sales and marketing strategy, existing planning permission, space for expansion, staff, wine reputation and what is included in the sale (such as the library wine stock) is essential. Sometimes existing vineyards are not as expensive as one is led to believe. For example two years ago a 2.79-acre plot of land in Combe Hay near Bath, which included a one-acre vineyard (enough to deliver 1,000 bottles of wine a year), sold, prior to auction, and had a guide price of £15,000. If the land had gone to auction it would probably have been sold for far more. Generally, a large acreage of land with grapevines already planted can double its agricultural value. This is especially true if it is in the right location with well-tended vines, the correct trellis system, and good clones and rootstocks. Google Earth maps can be a good starting point when looking for vineyards and land to buy.

Leasing a vineyard

There are occasionally opportunities in the UK to lease an existing vineyard, but they are few and far between. If entering into this type of agreement it is important to have a signed contract with the vineyard owner. This is a very different arrangement to the "lease a vine" scheme detailed in Chapter 6. Registration on the vineyard register is still required, and there have been occasions where no money has changed hands due to the leaseholder requiring bottles of wine in payment instead. This can suit someone who can no longer commit to the vineyard work but does not want to sell the land. The grapes could either be sold to a winery, or the winery could be the contract winemakers and return the bottled and labelled wine to the vineyard. Alternatively, you could buy in grapes from a vineyard and approach a winery to make the wine, but that takes all the fun out of it!

Buying land to plant a vineyard

Selecting a suitable and appropriate vineyard site is the most important aspect of setting up a vineyard. There are vineyard consultants and land agents in the UK that can help, but preliminary investigations can easily be carried out by potential land-buyers themselves. With the knowledge and understanding of the impact of the correct altitude, aspect, soil, drainage, frost and wind protection, initial land searches by individuals can be undertaken. The size of the vineyard land required is the immediate factor to consider, ensuring that the vineyard is manageable. To allow for future expansion, make sure that additional adjacent land is available. Additional considerations when seeking potential vineyard sites include space for a winery, road access, proximity to residential property and waste disposal facilities. Buying land with planning permission or existing agricultural building/s is extremely beneficial especially when seeking legal planning consent for a winery. Planning permission regulations and legal requirements are detailed on the Government website **www.direct.gov.uk/en/HomeAndCommunity/Planning/PlanningPermission/DG_4018203**. It must be remembered that building regulations are a separate issue to planning regulations. Guidance can also be sought from established UK vineyards that have already been through the planning application process. Residential properties close to a vineyard site may raise concerns about the construction of new winery buildings due to high noise and traffic, especially during harvest with long working hours, and delivery and collection of wine and equipment. It is important to do a detailed feasibility study when considering vineyard site purchase as it allows the buyer to approach the project with a complete understanding of the initial outlay and long-term investment, as well as predicted income. As a guide to land prices in the South East, in February 2012 suitable sites for a vineyard in Kent were advertised for sale by Strutt and Parker. Three lots had a guide price in excess of £10,000 per acre and the fourth plot had a guide price of £20,000 per acre.

Vines take time to establish and develop so it is unlikely that the new vineyard owner will see any income for five to seven years in the case of sparkling wine production, possibly earlier for still wines. In the UK the predicted budget is approximately £5,000 per acre to plant and establish a vineyard. This includes grapevines, posts and trellis system, but does not include the cost of buying machinery, labour costs or consultancy fees.

Site assessment

In the northern hemisphere the best vineyard sites have a south-facing orientation, for maximum sunlight throughout the growing season. It is important to investigate the climate of the site, particularly growing degree days (GDD). These are the number of days in the grapevine growing season above 10°C. It is a system that is commonly used to determine grape variety suitability for an area that will provide enough heat for the grapes to ripen. It can be useful to check the site temperatures for the past 10 to 15 years to learn about the lowest recorded temperatures experienced. These will give an indication of the frost risk, but if the site does not have a weather station, or the data is not readily available from the seller, then use the nearest weather station information. It is important to find out what the land was previously used for, what other crops are planted nearby, and if there is a local vineyard in the vicinity. Some crops may encourage grapevine pests or disease, and the possibility of chemical spray drift from neighbouring properties should be considered. Study the general geography of the land, as a small very steep slope on one side could cause problems for labour, machinery and grape berry ripening. Once land has been identified, enquire about the main local pests such as rabbits and deer, as it is important to establish whether deer fences will need to be installed. Although if rabbits are the main pest, fencing to deter them is not the only method of control, nor do you have to use toxic substances, as organic methods for rabbit control are available (*see* Chapter 3).

Slope In the cool UK climate elevation is important as grape acidity increases as the altitude increases. A slope of above 5 per cent is recommended at 100m above sea level. The slope should be enough to provide drainage of cold air, which is important when spring frosts occur and allows for water drainage. Cold air is heavier than warm air so settles on the low land, and cold air moves quicker downhill when a slope is steep. It is important not to have barriers such as trees blocking the path of the cold air, so they should be removed as part of the site preparation prior to planting. Although successful steep slope viticulture can be found in some wine regions, specifically in the Rheingau in Germany where special equipment is being developed to carry out vineyard work, extremely steep slopes cause problems for vineyard personnel and machinery in the UK, due to the dangers of operating machinery on steep slopes, as well as an increase in the possibility of soil erosion.

Aspect The aspect or direction of a vineyard slope in the UK, where summers are cool and GDD is low, is south facing (south, south-east or south-west) to permit heat accumulation for grape berry development and ripening. South-facing vineyards in Europe warm earlier in the spring, and grapevines will warm more on sunny days when they are facing south than on a north-facing site. Occasionally trunk injury or bark splitting on the south-west sides of vines occurs, due to the vine parts being warm on sunlit winter days followed by quick chilling. Vineyards with an east part (SE) benefit from the morning sun and dry quicker from rain and dew than a west-facing slope, which reduces disease incidence.

Previous land use It is important to find out what the land was used for before it is planted, in order to find out whether it is compatible with the growing of grapevines. It is a good idea to list the entire past crop and/or animal use and management practices, along with past herbicide use. This is an important aspect of vineyard site selection, as considerations must be made for pesticide or fungicide residues: some agricultural sprays can stay in the soil for a long time and be toxic to new vines. In addition any soil adjustments and pest problems need to be dealt with on every part of the site. Find out if the site has ever been altered or levelled in any way: some trees and plants, especially oak trees, can leave behind rot diseases in leftover roots, so sites that were previously forest should lay fallow for one year (preferably three to five years) to decrease the fungal inoculum in the soil.

Soil and drainage Soil tests to determine soil type, texture, soil depth, fertility/nutrition and soil water holding capacity, are of the utmost importance, as these factors determine how it will be treated and managed. The soil profile is determined by digging a pit and taking soil samples at 0-30cm and 30-100cm, to test the topsoil and subsoil. Soil samples must be taken across the site. The amount of samples will be dependent on the size of the site, but usually 15

Case study: Greyfriars Vineyard, Surrey: Mike Wagstaff

Mike Wagstaff first became intrigued by the potential of growing grapes and making wine in England six years ago, after picking up a copy of Richard Selley's book. Richard Selley had been his geology lecturer at Imperial College in the early 1980s. At the time, Mike had a full-time job running an Aberdeen-based oil company, and ended up carrying the book in his briefcase for several years. It was not until the company was taken over in 2009 that he and his wife had the time and capital to think more seriously about owning a vineyard.

They spent six months researching the question 'Can you make money from an English vineyard?" It was important to them that any investment was commercially viable. They started looking for a site and were expecting to find somewhere on the South Downs in Sussex. They knew of the existence of Greyfriars, Puttenham, on the North Downs outside Guildford, and at the same time became aware that it was up for sale. It took nearly another six months from first viewing to purchase, while they completed the legal due diligence and put together the business plan for Greyfriars.

Unsurprisingly, they found that buying an existing vineyard rather than starting from scratch has a number of advantages and disadvantages. On the positive side, an existing vineyard has a track record of producing quality grapes and/or wines. In the case of Greyfriars it had been planted 20 years before, so there was a history of successfully growing Pinot noir and Chardonnay on the site. In addition, most of the teething issues related to starting any new venture should have been solved, and as a going concern it should come with some existing vineyard and/or winery infrastructure and equipment. It also gets you into business from day one, rather than having to wait up to five years or more before the possibility of cash coming in. Perhaps most importantly, there is a stock of local vineyard 'expertise', which is the sum of a lot of small things, many of which are site specific and take a number of years to build up. When buying an existing vineyard it is important to put in place an appropriate mechanism to facilitate the transfer of this expertise.

On the negative side, buying an existing vineyard as a going concern probably requires a larger up-front investment than simply purchasing land. Also one is 'stuck' with the previous owner's vine varietal and clone selection, planting and trellising system. What were fashionable 10 or 20 years ago may not work today, since we have seen huge changes in vineyard technology and tastes in wine over this time.

Overall when buying an existing location, it is critical to ensure that the fundamentals of the vineyard are sound and to understand what works and why? It is also vital to identify which areas of the vineyard can be improved and how you plan to do this. In the case of Greyfriars, virtually all of the areas for improvement were ultimately due to a lack of capital, energy and ambition for the vineyard, which are all things which can be solved over time with the application of energy, and of course money.

In getting into the vineyard business it was always critical for Mike that it would be a viable stand-alone commercial venture. In England, because of the small size of our industry and the fact that it is spread over a large area, we lack the infrastructure and expertise which is readily available in major wine-producing regions. As a result the minimum critical size required to operate a commercially viable vineyard is probably larger than in most other wine-producing regions, in order to support the necessary investment in equipment and organisation. Greyfriars' existing vineyard was small at ~0.5ha, but it was vital to Mike that they had the space to expand to get to the critical size to support the necessary investment in vineyard equipment, tractor, sprayers, etc. Like any business, the scarcest and most expensive resource in the vineyard is high-quality and reliable personnel. Mike also firmly believes it is critical to invest in as much automation as possible, in order to reduce the exposure to personnel risk. Business economics dictate that you spread this investment over as many vines as possible. The total size of the property is just over 12ha, with just over 8ha viable for planting vines, large enough to create a commercially viable vineyard but small enough to be manageable.

Greyfriars, like most of the vineyards in the south of England lies within an area with significant planning restrictions. While on purchase they did not have planning permission to expand substantially, the stock of buildings and barns on the property gives them plenty of space for the time being, and it means that they will be redeveloping existing buildings in due course rather than building on a 'greenfield' site. The legal aspects of the purchase were particularly complex because the property is also home to four vets' practices and cottages with tenants, which added a commercial property perspective. There were moments when they seriously doubted the wisdom of proceeding. As a result the principal item that Mike would change with the benefit of hindsight is the length of time it took to complete the purchase, which was from May to November. During this period, while they were able to plan, they were unable to make significant commitments for new vines or equipment, and because of the seasonal nature of the business, they missed the deadline for ordering high graft vines for planting the next year.

For the first year, they made minimal changes to the existing vineyard, in order to understand properly what they had inherited. The vineyard was planted with Chardonnay (85 per cent) and Pinot noir (15 per cent); the core of future plantings was for sparkling wine so there was no need to change grape varieties. The existing vines were in good condition despite their age, although a small proportion will need to be replaced over the next year or two. While they are not changing the training system from Double Guyot, they have replaced the entire trellising in the existing vineyard: changing from wooden posts to steel. While wooden posts are more picturesque, after replacing 20 per cent of the posts over the winter of 2010/11, and faced with the prospect of changing another 50 per cent during the winter of 2011/12, sticking with wooden posts was not a realistic option.

In the UK, if you buy an existing vineyard you will probably not be acquiring a long history and, since we are not yet restricted on new plantings, the benefits of an existing vineyard are not obvious. Although acquiring an existing site will give you a flying start in comparison with a brand new site, it is absolutely critical to do your research and have a clear plan about how you are going to change operations, no matter how well the existing vineyard is running. It is certain that you will end up changing a lot more things than you expect, which will have a subsequent impact on costs and timing. Like any project, everything costs more and takes longer than you could possibly imagine.

www.greyfriarsvineyard.com

to 20 samples are taken on a 12-hectare site. All non-uniform areas should be tested, including hills or dips. A soil report can include organic matter, soil colour, texture, rock (amount, size and type), soil structure and particle aggregation, soil porosity and approximate moisture content, plus relevant comments such as signs of poor drainage. Geographic Information Systems (GIS) software and Global Positioning Satellite (GPS) data to create thematic maps is used by some viticulture or soil consultants. Additionally Laverstoke Farm Park in Hampshire has a fully equipped comprehensive analytical chemistry laboratory for soil and food analysis **www.laverstokepark.co.uk/soil_testing_laboratory.asp**x. It is essential that soil analysis results are correctly interpreted so a soil treatment plan can be prepared before planting any vines. *Vitis vinifera* roots prefer soils of pH 6 to 7, but sparkling wine grape varieties favour a pH of 6.5 as it can affect grape acidity levels and therefore the acidity of the final wine. High pH levels limit nutrient availability of phosphorus, iron, manganese, boron, copper and zinc, although rootstock selection can ease the problem slightly. Soil liming before planting can also alleviate the root zone problem, but soil pH will have to be monitored through the life of the vineyard, since acidity from untreated areas will eventually affect treated soil, reducing the pH. Excessive nitrogen in the soil of a site should be avoided, or planted with a plant that will remove/compete for the excessive nitrogen. Nitrogen, potassium, phosphorous, calcium, magnesium and sulphur are macro-nutrients in soil essential for grapevine growth. The micro-nutrients include chlorine, iron, boron, manganese, zinc, copper and molybdenum. Both excess and a deficiency of these nutrients cause visible symptoms in grapevines, can affect grape berry ripening, and can have implications for winemaking. Phosphorous levels in soils in the UK for grapevines should be 50ppm, potassium levels should be 200ppm, magnesium 110ppm and the potassium to magnesium ratio (K:Mg) should be 2:1. Nutrient-deficient soils can take a minimum of three years to correct, and should be factored into the site preparation before planting. Certain pest nematodes may cause problems in vineyards, and populations are typically higher in sandy soils. It is wise to have the soil tested for nematodes before site selection and planting.

Vineyard water drainage is important, as grapevines do not like wet feet because too much water limits the amount of oxygen available to the root system. Poor soil drainage means soil takes longer to warm up in spring; restricts root growth, which leads to a reduction in drought resistance and mineral deficiency; increases soil compaction; increases grapevine fungal diseases; and causes berry swelling and juice dilution. Agricultural drainage systems can be installed prior to planting grapevines. To improve soil drainage, ditches can be dug on the site, drainage pipe systems installed, and sub-soiling carried out if required. Subsurface water can be removed using tiling, which is a system of perforated plastic pipes fitted under the vineyard. Subsoil drainage uses a plastic pipe, called a drain tile, at a recommended depth in the soil, then surplus water flows into the drain tile to a ditch. If the vineyard site needs to have a drainage system installed prior to planting, then use a qualified, experienced agricultural drainage engineer. Remember that the water that drains off the vineyard site must comply with local water authority guidelines. Mole drains are another form of drainage similar to tiling but without the tile itself being installed. They are cheaper to install, but have a limited life. Soils must be at least 30 per cent clay and 40 per cent silt for the channel to remain steady for a couple of years, and have hardly any machinery traffic passing down the rows.

Site preparation

Soil preparation is especially important as the correct pH, soil nutrition levels, drainage, soil compaction level and soil texture will increase the chances of the young vines survival in the early years. Any soil additions that are needed and advised on your soil report, such as nutrient additions including lime, must be carried out prior to planting vines. If a cover crop is required to improve soil nutrient levels for alleyways between vine rows these may need to be established in advance of planting vines too. Some plants or trees around the edge of the site that are not suitable for wind breaks may need to be removed to prevent shading of the grapevines, minimise pests and disease incidence and improve air flow in the vineyard. Living wind breaks such as trees need to be installed early to allow them to grow prior to planting any grapevines. Large rocks can cause problems when planting vines especially when installing posts for training systems, therefore rocks, unwanted trees, perennial weeds and other unwanted debris need to be removed. This might need heavy equipment depending on the vineyard size and amount of work needed but could be carried out with the help of a local farmer or local contractor. Weed removal can be carried out with glyphosate weed killer spray depending on the vineyard size; however some weeds can take longer than a year to eradicate completely from the site. It is advisable to investigate which pests are common in the local area i.e. rabbits, deer or badgers, and a pest management strategy considered including the erection of a deer fence if necessary.

Windbreaks The dominant winds in the UK are the south-west wind, which causes rain but is quite mild, the easterly wind, which is dry and warm in summer but cold in winter, the southerly wind, which is hot and dry with thunderstorms, and the north-westerly winds, which are cold with rain showers and snow in winter. Wind will cool the microclimate of the grape clusters and cause damage to vines and trellis systems. However, living windbreaks compete with grapevines for soil space, water and nutrients, can increase vine shading, increase frost risk, and have a cost implication to plant/sustain as well as being home to birds that will be vineyard pests. Windbreaks are also beneficial as they can reduce wind damage, increase clusters per shoot by increasing fruitset and yield, produce larger leaves, increase vine productivity and reduce spray drift. It may be possible to plant several rows of windbreak trees using various species. Alternatively artificial windbreaks can be constructed using polyethylene netting on posts or planks of wood which do not have to be maintained. However, their initial cost is higher than buying trees, and they can degrade over time. There are some sites in the UK that do not need windbreaks, so they are not necessary for every vineyard.

Grape varieties

It is crucial to select the wine style required and the varieties suitable for the UK prior to starting any vineyard site planning. The intended wine style will impact on the choice of training system, pruning techniques and vineyard practices. Whilst the current tendency in the UK is for sparkling wine production, there are an increasing number of impressive still wines being produced from varieties such as Bacchus, Pinot noir and Pinot gris. There are an increasing number of brave UK grape-growers that are quietly experimenting with new technology, new production techniques, grape varieties new to the UK and new wine styles, with exciting and promising results. However, if the vineyard is being established specifically to grow grapes to sell to a winery, then it is important to ensure that the varieties to be planted are required by those buying the grapes. The list of varieties provided below is not a complete list of those accessible to the UK. A comprehensive list can be found on the DEFRA website **www.defra.gov.uk/food-farm/food/protected-names/uk-registered-names/** in the Protected Designation of Origin (PDO), Protected Geographical Indication (PGI) scheme details.

- **Red varieties**: Pinot noir, Regent, Rondo, Acolon, Cabernet cortis, Dornfelder, Dunkelfelder, Pinot meunier, Triomphe.
- **White varieties**: Bacchus, Madeleine Angevine, Orion, Phoenix , Pinot gris, Reichensteiner, Seyval blanc, Solaris, Auxerrois, Chardonnay, Chasselas blanc, Huxelrebe, Ortega, Pinot blanc, Schönburger, Siegerrebe, Gewürztraminer, Kerner, Müller-Thurgau, Riesling, Silvaner.

Rootstocks

There is a tendency to plant a range of rootstock and clone combinations and "hedge your bets" to ascertain which ones are the most suitable for the UK soil and site. However, it is far better to take the time to match the soil type and our cool UK climate to the best possible combination for the grape variety and site being planted. Far more clones are available for Chardonnay and Pinot noir than any other grape varieties currently being planted in the UK.

The use of vines grafted onto rootstocks is now common in wine regions due to the Phylloxera vastatrix louse which was identified in Europe in 1863. Inadvertently brought to Europe from the USA in the late 19th century, it destroyed two-thirds of European vineyards. In 1872, it was revealed that the roots of American grapevine species were not affected and *Vitis vinifera* was grafted onto American vine species. The only other effective remedies for Phylloxera are growing vines on sandy soils, or flooding the vineyard for 40 days a year, neither of which is suitable for existing UK vineyards.

Rootstocks have different levels of vigour and can take up nutrients at different speeds, affecting grapevine growth and vigour. High vigour plants have greater yield, longer growth cycles, lower sugar and higher acid levels, and are more vulnerable to disease. Also, rootstocks have different susceptibilities to nematodes which carry plant viruses. The majority of rootstocks used today originate from crosses of three American species *Vitis riparia, Vitis rupestris* and *Vitis berlandieri. Vitis riparia* rootstocks are low in vigour, and suffer from iron deficiency (chlorosis) in chalky soils. *Vitis rupestris* rootstocks are very vigorous, with a deep rooting system, but are also very susceptible to chlorosis. *Vitis berlandieri* is very vigorous and deep rooting and has a high resistance to chlorosis. Its cuttings have a very poor ability to root, and so it is rarely used as a pure species. The correct choice of rootstock for a vineyard depends on many factors, including the calcium content of the soil, the vigour of the vine required, the depth of soil, water-holding capacity of the soil, soil acidity and salinity, grape variety, climate and yield and quality required. The principal rootstocks used in the UK are 5BB, SO4, 5C and 125AA. Research is underway to investigate other available ones suitable for UK climate and soils. The rootstocks included in the table are all *Vitis riparia* x *Vitis berlandieri* hybrids.

Prices per vine decrease as the order volume increases, and with large orders of 2,000 or more delivery is often free in the UK. Grapevines are usually imported in parcels of 25 and have plant passports attached which must be kept for one year. In the UK there is a choice of high- or low-grafted vines which can increase growth and give more protection from rabbits. To date there is no supplier available in the UK that supplies organic grapevines grafted to organically grown rootstocks or genetically modified clones and rootstocks.

Rootstock	Description
5BB	Very vigorous and suited to a very wide range of soils, including poor soils (humid, compact, clay, shallow) where high vigour is needed. Suitable for low-density systems, such as GDC, and often used with Seyval blanc, this is a weakly vigorous, but strongly flowering cultivar.
125AA	Particularly useful for soils which are poorly drained or for poor stony dry soils, but not heavy clay.
5C/Kober 5C	Suitable for a wide range of soil types, including deep, fertile, well-drained clay, but not for extremely dry soils. More vigorous than 101-14 or 3309. Good for wide row spacing.
SO4	A bit less vigorous than 5C, but suited to a very wide range of soil types, particularly fertile, humid soils and light well-drained soils. It can have problems with magnesium uptake which affects leaf photosynthesis (Mg is the centre of the chlorophyll molecule) so may require foliar feeding. More vigorous than 101-14 or 3309, good for wide row-spacing.
Further rootstocks that could be of use to the UK and could be considered are:	**Description**
101-14	Good for deep soils particularly clay, poor drainage and good water-holding capacity. Moderate-vigour and good for close vine spacing.
3309C	Good for deep well-drained soils with good water holding capacity. Performs well in close vine-spacing and advances maturity ahead but not as much as 101-14. Moderate vigour.
161-49C/161-49 Couderc	Low-vigour rootstock with a strong tolerance of lime. Useful for high density plantings.
420A/Millardet et de Grasset	Low-vigour rootstock on most soils; much less vigorous than the related rootstocks Kober 5C and 5BB. It is difficult to graft and root resulting in some vines not growing and nursery shortages. Prone to potassium deficiency, tolerant of lime but its nematode resistance is not known.

Rootstock data includes information provided by Chris Foss, Plumpton College.

Clones

Clones are genetically identical to the parent, which is usually propagated using cuttings. Clonal selection was first carried out by Froehlich in 1896 on Sylvaner. Until the 1950s, it was almost exclusively carried out in Germany, but is now also done in France by ENTAV (Etablissement National pour l'Amélioration de la Viticulture) and by INRA (Institut National de la Recherche Agricole). Important selection considerations include average yield, bud fertility, early or late budburst, early or late ripening, berry size, berry sugar and acidity, phenolic and aroma compounds, disease resistance, drought resistance, frost resistance, organoleptic quality and virus free. Some clones are only appropriate for specific regions, which can lead to over production in some areas and a decrease in diverse genetic material. These days grapevine clonal selection has reduced the use of other vine propagation techniques such as mass selection, hybridisation and intraspecific hybrids.

The most common clones for sparkling wine production in the UK that Vine Works Ltd **www.vine-works.com** recommends are;

- **Chardonnay - 95, 76** (high quality, low yield), **96, 121** (good quality, good yield). These are the most widely planted Chardonnay clones in Champagne.
- **Pinot noir – 777** (small, compact cluster, small berries, low yielding), **828** (high quality, low yield), **943** (the berries are the smallest of all the Dijon clones, low seed counts, small clusters, open bunches, low yields, higher sugar content), **GM20/13** (German clone with open bunches and lower acidity).
- **Pinot meunier – 977, 865, 864** (heavy cropping clones).

The most common and popular Pinot noir wine clones in Burgundy are 777 and 828, and the reliable 115 and 667, all of which are available for still Pinot noir wine production in the UK. There are many more clones available and the best starting point to match clone and rootstock combination is the ENTAV international catalogue - 'Catalogue of Selected Varieties & Certified Clones Cultivated in France'.

www.entav.com/ANG/index.htm. There are many clones available for Pinot noir and Chardonnay, but fewer for other grape varieties i.e. Bacchus, which has demonstrated hardly any differences amongst clones in the UK, but is affected more by site, canopy management and crop levels. All French certified varieties and clones are listed in the ENTAV catalogue, although not all will be suitable for UK soil and climate conditions. It is extremely important to store the grapevines correctly in a cool, dark area when they arrive and before planting. Additionally they should be checked on arrival for adequate moisture and lack of mould. Roots must be soaked in water for 12 to 24 hours prior to planting in the vineyard.

Grafted grapevine suppliers

Pepinieres Tourette, Les Granges 07 200 Vogue, France
www.pepinieres-tourette.fr/en
Stephen Skelton MW, 1B Lettice Street, London, SW6 4EH
www.englishwine.com
The Vine House, Farfield Farm, Westow, York, YO60 7LS
www.thevinehouse.co.uk
Vine & Wine Ltd, Orchard Croft, Putley Ledbury, Herefordshire, HR8 2RG **www.vineandwine.co.uk**
Vine Works Ltd, 7 Steele Close, The Juggs, West Chiltington, West Sussex, RH20 2LL **www.vine-works.com**
Vines Direct Ltd, 13 Ferneham Road, Fareham, Hants, PO15 5BT
www.vinesdirect.co.uk
Vineyard Solutions Ltd, Unit 11a, Baddow Park Estate, Great Baddow, Chelmsford, Essex, CM2 7SY **www.vineyardsolutions.co.uk**

Vineyard design

After the site and grape varieties have been chosen, the vital decisions are grapevine spacing and density, and the choice of trellis / training system. These elements impact capital outlay, along with the vineyard site characteristics, so will directly affect the vineyard management of the site. Firstly make sure the row orientation is downhill, north to south to allow for maximum sunlight exposure, and to assist with cold air flow and to prevent machinery, especially tractors, from rolling over. Decisions regarding planting density (which includes row spacing and vine spacing) should take into account the use of machinery for end of row turning and the width of tractor implements, as well as soil type, rootstock, grape variety and type of trellis system to be installed. There are many trellis systems available, but the Vertical Shoot Positioned (VSP) system i.e. single and double guyot, is common in the UK; other systems also employed are the Scott Henry, Geneva Double Curtain (GDC), Sylvoz and the less common Chablis system. The choice of training system to be established will need to be made in conjunction with the choice of pruning style: either cane or spur pruning. Row length is also important because long rows of vines are difficult for employees to work in. It is worth developing a vineyard map with as much detail as possible regarding blocks of varieties and their location with the clones/rootstock combination before marking out and planting the vineyard.

Planting grapevines

It is important not to plant on hot, sunny, windy days as roots can be damaged during the planting process in those conditions. Make sure there is a short time between grapevines arriving and the planting taking place, and that the vines are stored correctly. If the vineyard is relatively small then you may choose to mark out the rows and spacing before planting the vines by hand with help from friends and family. With medium to large UK vineyards it is more common now to use machine planting, using GPS and laser-guided equipment with a planting plan. It is important to remember that it is more critical to have prepared the site correctly if using a machine to plant the vines.

If hand planting, remember to make sure the hole is large enough for the root system without damaging any part of it, and place soil around the vines, mounded, to stop any fertiliser/herbicide from damaging the young vines. If the spring is a warm dry season then the newly planted vines will need watering to avoid water stress. Consideration should be given to the use of grow tubes/tree guards/vine shelters which promote rapid shoot growth (but with long internodes) early in the season, from the greenhouse-effect created inside the tube. It has been suggested that they encourage the vine to pro-

Case study: Hobdens Vineyards, East Sussex: Gerard and Jonica Fox, site and soil preparation pre-planting

In 2003 Gerard and Jonica Fox decided to plant a vineyard. That meant understanding the soil, the micro-climate and the drainage. By the time they had completed the planning and preparation (18 months) they were ready to plant on 5th May 2005.

They made some instant key decisions: to make sparkling wines; to plant vines of the same varieties as those approved for champagne; to have rootstock which could cope with cool summers and clay soils, so they used SO4 (workhorse of cool climates albeit with some issues) and 3309C (clay friendly /fruit quality enhancing) to see if there was any quantitative difference in fruit quality or crop weights; to have mid-season ripening clones (late clones might never ripen and early clones might make harvest /winemaking logistics difficult).

They looked at pruning styles in books and in vineyards and worked out their trellising plan. They set their fruiting wire height quite high, not so much due to viticultural reasons but more to do with being 6ft tall, although it also keeps the fruit and young shoots safer from a ground frost.

Having decided that the fruiting wire would be at 1m, it followed that the trellis height would be about 2m and that then led to relatively wide alleys at 2.3m (on later plantings this was reduced to 2.1m to increase density). Vines were planted 1.5m apart (later plantings: 1.25m) so the first field is less dense than many other English vineyards. Jonica is a keen supporter of yield-per-vine rather than yield-per-hectare data. 2.1m is a better width for them: not just for density but also for mowing, as it keeps the central strip of grass fully trimmed. It is important to think about the equipment you will need to use before you set your alley width forever.

Their first field of vines has a 7 per cent slope, faces south-south-east and is thick Wealden clay over sandstone. Clay depths vary across the vineyard from 35m+ to just 2m in one corner. Iron-rich gravels are spread in thin-layered pockets across the field at depths of 1.5m or more. Topsoils were loamy and about 15cm to 25cm deep, and the correct pH level of 6.5. Lying on the mid-slope of a substantial hill (the vineyard is 380m above sea level), this was quite wet land due to run-off from uphill.

The site is sheltered, with light summer winds to keep the air moving, but protected from westerly gales and north-easterly winter winds. The existing hedges and individual trees within the hedgerows provide all the shelter required, although they did lift the canopy and reduce the height of five oak trees to improve light and air flow. Frost and cold air drains well, and they keep the downhill woodland cleared of undergrowth so that icy air is not trapped in the field.

Soil preparation was extremely important. First they installed drainage, a herringbone pattern, 15cm diameter perforated plastic drains laid in gravel meant 25cm wide, 1.45m deep trenches, a layer of stone, the pipe then more stone, backfilled with soil every 3m across the slope. The drainage improved immediately, but there was significant compaction from the heavy vehicles and materials that needed to be addressed so they subsoiled the field at its driest point in August 2004, breaking up the compaction and opening up the deeper soil.

In September 2004, the field was sprayed with glyphosphate, whilst the air temperatures remained warm enough to maintain photosynthesis and ensure the chemical was transported in the sap. In October they were lucky enough to have help from a local farmer who ploughed the field, as they did not own a tractor or any equipment themselves. The vegetation was left to rot and the soils to break up via frost action and weathering over winter.

The timing of the next stage was critical because if a power harrow is used too early and it rains the result is erosion and/or an implantable swamp. If it is done too late then planting is delayed and costs increased. They checked weather forecasts and ran the power harrow over the land the day before planting. Being clay and ex-meadowland meant they needed to work hard to create a smooth area for machine planting using laser/wire guidance. They harrowed in two directions the day before and harrowed again on the day, running ahead of the JCB Fast-trac mounted planting machine. Despite this care they still had some lumps of root-bound top soil that meant a few vines had to be removed and hand planted. Within half a day they had just under 4,000 vines in the ground waiting for their support canes and protective vine-guards to be installed before they started to bud. They thought they had about four or five days to get this finished if the sunny weather continued. They found that laser-guided planting is good but not infallible. If the wind blows against the wire, the land is un-even, the soil preparation too lumpy or measurements are not taken accurately, rows may be straight but too narrow at one end, or not be the right width, unless close attention is paid to setting out. Each row must be measured carefully.

They trellised the vineyard almost immediately. Early trellising meant they had the fruiting wire in place to tie the tutor to, minimising the risk of vines blowing over or getting pulled over by rabbits. They did not expect deer, so found out the heart-breaking way that young vine shoots are gourmet food for deer. Expensive deer fencing went up very fast at that point!

Their trellising options were DIY, which is not easy with no experience and no equipment, or get some help. They decided on a fencing contractor to do the post-banging and install the first fruiting wire, and then carried on from there. They installed two fruiting wires, and found they really only needed one. By the time they planted their second field there were UK-based specialist trellising companies available.

Was all the preparation worth it? By the end of 2005 they had "lost" only 5 vines; in 2012 that number had risen to 25 dead or weak vines: a 0.026 per cent failure rate that they can live with!

www.hobdensvineyards.com

PrintWeek
2011 AWARDS
Winner
Label printer of the year

duce a crop in the second year, but it has also been shown to decrease overall vine growth by limiting the vine to one shoot. In many cases these tubes decrease leaf area in the first year of growth, but are useful to protect the young vines from rabbits and contact herbicide sprays. Lack of pruning or bad pruning in the first year will mean the vines will have too many buds, and allowing vines to have grape bunches too early in their lives will affect the growth of the vascular system and root growth. In some wine regions i.e. California, it has been established that young vine death is frequently connected with grapevines that were allowed to produce fruit in their second or third year.

Single stakes and string can be used to support the shoots in the first year, and then in the second year the cane that will become the trunk should be selected and unwanted buds removed and cordons established. The trellis system must be able to hold the weight of the fully grown vine, and withstand wind and machinery between the rows. It is imperative to have strong posts at the end of the rows to anchor the entire row and vines. The anchor system can be an "H" shape or a slanted system, used in conjunction with high tensile wire which can be twisted and tied more easily than galvanised steel wire, due to its increased strength and durability. Another consideration is the type of posts to use for the trellis system, as wooden posts can be more aesthetically pleasing than steel ones but can eventually rot and need replacing sooner than steel posts. The final decision with regards to trellis system and the materials used will be due to grape variety, canopy management, machinery usage and overall costs.

During the first two years, the vines must be trained properly, weeds must be controlled, vines must have access to adequate nutrients, and diseases and insects controlled. Once planted the vines should be sprayed with fungicides every two weeks in the UK to prevent fungal infections in the first year of growth. Additionally a suitable frost protection system should be installed to prevent frost damage to young vines that makes them susceptible to disease (*see* Chapter 3).

Vineyard equipment

Not all vineyard equipment needs to be purchased in the first year of

Case study: Stopham Vineyard, West Sussex: Making Still Wine by Simon Woodhead

It has been argued that still wine production in England is unsustainable. It is fair to say that we are not in the perfect winemaking climate, which can affect yields. In his first year he had frost, and last year in June very heavy rain knocked the flowers off the vines, reducing yields by over half, yet Simon Woodhead believes that still wine production can be sustainable as long as you make top-quality wine. Whilst yields are crucial, quality brings demand and, with demand, profitable pricing. His first vintage was in 2010 and was well received in The Times, The Observer, and more recently by Jancis Robinson **www.jancisrobinson.com/articles/a201202161**. Apparently the 2011 vintage currently in the tanks is set to taste even better. Simon believes the only way to achieve good-quality wine is to obsess about the detail.

When he looks back over the last five years it helps to use recognisable grape varieties and premium packaging, and find a market, perhaps via a good distributor, that will pay a profitable price. It also helps to have an amazing assistant like Tom Bartlett, and an invaluable winemaking consultant and mentor, David Cowderoy. There are so many pitfalls, so for each decision and process, ask yourself what will improve and protect the wine.

In the winery, he set fermentations to last between four to six weeks using a closed loop temperature control system: It therefore helps to preserve the delicate aromatic characteristics of English wine. A laboratory is needed to measure SO2, pH and acidity, but also for crucial blending and fining trials to remove bitterness and astringency from the wine. Finally, an inert gas sterile bottler ("monoblock") is vital to protect the aromas. This helps prevent oxidation and bacteria in wine. Still wine production in England can be sustainable and rewarding as long as you are passionate in your pursuit of excellent wine.

Stopham Vineyard was planted in 2007 at Stopham, Pulborough.
www.stophamvineyard.co.uk/bottling.htm

establishing the vineyard. Equipment should be included in the long-term business plan, and second-hand equipment is often available from dealers, some of which appear in Farmers Weekly magazine or are UKVA members. There are some online retailers that sell and hire vineyard equipment, such as **www.vitifruitequipment.co.uk**, based in Kent. Make sure that spare parts for any vineyard machinery are available for the foreseeable future in case of breakdown. Vineyard equipment needed will depend on the size of the site and the vineyard design, but can include tractors, lawnmowers, flail-mowers, quad bikes, leaf removers and spray equipment. The materials for planting and the trellis system can be purchased from consultants and suppliers listed in this chapter. When choosing a vineyard consultant it is advisable to speak to other local grape-growers for recommendations. Furthermore, choose a consultant who has practical vineyard management experience as well as an academic qualification in viticulture and oenology, because it is important that they fully understand the effects of environmental influences as well as cultural practices on the short- and long-term growth of the vine and grape berry development.

Vineyard planning and management

It has been known to take two to three years, and in some cases longer, to locate a suitable vineyard site, but when the site has been found the planning must start immediately. Diary planning must include financial organisation, a business plan, the gathering of local climate data, the start of viticulture education, workshops to attend, consideration given to the hiring of a vineyard consultant, and site preparation needed prior to planting. It is worth bearing in mind GIS and GPS can be used to map soils, slope, aspect and other topographic details, and these maps help to plan the vineyard design. The data provided can be used to plan row direction, row length, vine-spacing, trellis design, soil additions, water and drainage, grape variety, clones and rootstocks. Farm insurance should be considered and, while NFU mutual is one company used by some vineyards, it can pay to investigate other companies. Additional costs to include in a business plan for the vineyard and/or winery should be agricultural staff wages, estimations of number of staff needed (this will depend on the vineyard's size), health and safety compliance, and first aiders. If no winery is being planned, then before planting the vines contact a winery to insure there is a market for the grapes, or a contract winery to make the wine. The vineyard owner will need to work closely with the winery to produce the quality of grapes they require. One thing that is often overlooked is the harvest operations and logistics, including getting the pickers on the days needed. Start setting up vineyards records straight away detailing spray dates, to include what was sprayed, concentration and volume, vine growth information and weather data.

UK Vineyard consultants

A'Court Viticulture, 4 Shinners Cottages, The Level, Dittisham, Dartmouth, Devon TQ6 0EN
www.acourtviticulture.co.uk

Clemens Gmbh and Co KG, Rudolf-Diesel-Straße 854516 Wittlich, Germany
www.clemens-online.com

Dr Richard Smart, Smart Viticulture, now based in Cornwall, UK
vinedoctor@smartvit.com.au, **www.smartvit.com.au**

FAST Ltd, Crop Technology Centre, Brogdale Farm, Faversham, Kent, ME13 8XZ
www.fastltd.co.uk

Fruits of Labour, Flat 4, St Davids Lodge, 39 Winchester Road, Worthing, BN11 4DH
www.fruits-of-labour.co.uk

Furleigh Estate (Wine Consultants) Ltd, Salway Ash, Bridport, Dorset, DT6 5JF, Tel 01308 488981
iemail@btinternet.com

John Buchan Agronomy, 1A Garden City, Tern Hill, Market Drayton, Shropshire TF9 3QB, Tel 01630 639875
johnab@ukf.net

Plumpton College, Ditchling Road, nr Lewes, Plumpton, East Sussex, BN7 3AE
www.plumpton.ac.uk

Three Choirs Vineyards Ltd, Newent, Gloucestershire, GL18 1LS
www.three-choirs-vineyards.co.uk

Stephen Skelton MW, 1B Lettice Street, London, SW6 4EH
www.englishwine.com

Vineyard Dynamics Ltd, 77 Pullman Lane, Godalming, Surrey, GU7 1YB
www.vineyarddynamics.com

The Vine House, Farfield Farm, Westow, York, YO60 7LS
www.thevinehouse.co.uk

Vine & Wine Ltd, Orchard Croft, Putley Ledbury, Herefordshire, HR8 2RG
www.vineandwine.co.uk

Vine Works Ltd, 7 Steele Close, The Juggs, West Chiltington, West Sussex, RH20 2LL
www.vine-works.com

Vines Direct Ltd, 13 Ferneham Road, Fareham, Hants, PO15 5BT
www.vinesdirect.co.uk

Vineyard Solutions Ltd, Unit 11a, Baddow Park Estate, Great Baddow, Chelmsford, Essex, CM2 7SY
www.vineyardsolutions.co.uk

Chapter Three

The grapes

Case Studies

The grapes

The principles of plant biology, science and chemistry help the winegrower to produce healthy grapes, quality wine and run a sustainable business. Generally UK winegrowers are very aware of their environmental responsibility, for example through the planting of native trees as a windbreak at the new Rathfinny Estate, East Sussex, and biodiversity trails being designed and wild flower meadows planted around the Avonleigh Organic Vineyard, Wiltshire, as a natural method of controlling insects and pests. However, this chapter does not explain every aspect of conventional, organic or biodynamic viticulture or winemaking in the UK, but instead focuses on UK regulations, certification, European law and grape-growing methods available to UK vineyards.

The annual grapevine growth cycle

The fruitful grapevine buds burst the year after their formation after the winter dormancy period, in spring when budburst happens and shoots emerge. The energy needed for this comes from the root-stored carbohydrates from the previous year. The grapevine annual growth cycle is dependent on many cultural and environmental factors but a general overview is listed below.

Seasonal vineyard activities

The correct timing and severity of seasonal vineyard practices is crucial. The planning of staffing requirements, record keeping, initiating a spray programme and ensuring equipment is maintained are all important considerations for the vineyard owner or manager. The vineyard year needs planning ahead and needs to be included in the original business plan detailing financial considerations for labour, equipment, sprays and consultancy fees.

Winter

The number of staff, costs and winter pruning technique (spur or cane) will be determined by the vineyard size, grape variety, wine style and the type of training system used. It is important that all staff

The annual grapevine growth cycle	
November - March	Grapevines enter into dormancy in November and begin to awaken in March when the soil (at a depth of 25 cm) reaches a temperature of just over 10° C.
April - May	Sap rises and bud burst occurs followed by shoot growth and the emergence of leaves, tendrils and inflorescences. Different grape varieties and clones will start bud burst at different times. Spring frost damage can destroy the crop.
June - July	When temperatures begin to rise, flowering occurs in late May to early June (early summer). Fruitset is when the vine has flowered and fertilisation has taken place.
August - October	The grapes start to change colour - veraison (ripening) from early August. Harvest occurs in the UK in September/October.

are trained in your pruning requirements to leave the correct amount of buds per vine for a balanced vine that meets crop levels. Pruning cuttings can be returned to the vineyard floor to add organic matter but can harbour diseases, or they can be burnt or pulverised (see the Environment Agency section). Double pruning involves pre-pruning in November/December, leaving six to ten buds on every spur (about 40cm long) and removing the cut sections. The second pruning is carried out in late February/March and is a method used to reduce Eutypa lata/Eutypa dieback in vines (not common in the UK). However, it can cause early budburst, increased frost damage risk and increased labour costs, and can reduce growth the following year. Only one UK vineyard currently does double pruning using a tractor mounted pre-pruning machine. Trellis maintenance is carried out at this time.

Spring

Tying down of this year's cane to the lower wire must be done as well as bud rubbing/removal on the trunks to reduce the growth of water shoots/suckers. Pruning should be complete by the end of March when fertiliser/manure is spread, soil nutrition applications are made, hoeing breaks up the soil, and new vines are planted. Some first sprays may be required against insects and fungal disease, and budburst signals the start of the new growing season!

Summer

In early summer the grapevine flowers emerge. After fruitset, canopy management (including leaf removal, mechanically or by hand) in the fruit zone is carried out to help with air flow, spray penetration and increase light into the fruit zone to achieve optimum ripening (not recommended until after fruitset). Shoot tipping/topping and tucking in of shoots is performed to maintain the desired canopy height and unwanted lateral growth around the fruiting zone is removed. A few UK vineyards have carried out green harvesting during veraison as the fruit changes colour, to retain clusters that are ripening evenly, but this depends on crop load and fruitset success levels. Further spraying is carried out, except during the four weeks leading up to harvest. The moveable wires are lifted up and spraying against diseases is done. This is the time for vintage preparation: cleaning of winery equipment, machinery maintenance, purchase of laboratory analysis equipment, ordering ingredients and employment of grape-pickers.

Autumn

Prior to harvesting, the grapes are sampled regularly to monitor sugar levels, pH and acidity levels (depending on the weather, but this can start in September). When they have reached the required levels for the wine style, including phenolic maturity, they will be picked, which is by hand in the UK (except at Denbies Estate, Surrey, who have a mechanical harvester), and wine production begins.

Organic grape-growing

Organic wine production is based upon modern, sustainable farming which maintains soil fertility and, as the EU explains, "combines best environmental practices, a high level of biodiversity, the preservation of natural resources, and a production method in line with the preference of certain consumers for products produced using natural substances and processes". An understanding of soil science, crop growing and ecology, gained from science research, has developed organic farming methods. Instead of being aware of the limits of chemical sprays, an organic vineyard owner needs to understand the causes of disease infections as well as the type, timing and concentration of treatments. In the UK the best known organic certification body is the Soil Association, but there are others including the Organic Farmers & Growers, and the Biodynamic Association. Each certification body has different standards and fee structure, as well as a different understanding of wine production. They all provide organic grape-growing standards that UK vineyards must adhere to for their accreditation, as well as advice and guidance.

The Soil Association Certification (SA Certification) is registered with Defra and has certified farms, foods and other products and processing as organic since 1973 under the terms of EU Regulation No. 834/2007. For processor schemes, the application fee is £548 (plus VAT). This includes the application fee, first inspection and full range of services for one year. The first full annual fee is payable one year after application and is based on the total organic wine sales in the first year. The full Soil Association organic standards for farming and growing were revised in January 2012 and can be found online at **www.sacert.org/fooddrink/stepstocertification**. Additionally, the association produces details of their fee structure in their information packs, and can be contacted by telephone (Tel 0117 914 2406) or via their website **www.soilassociation.org**.

Organic Farmers & Growers Ltd (OF&G) is another certification body accredited by Defra, and is approved to inspect organic production and processing in the UK. In addition, OF&G works with the Association for Organic Recycling (AfOR) and Renewable Energy Assurance Ltd (REAL) on the inspection and certification of compost and biofertiliser (from anaerobic digestion) respectively. The OF&G Organic Standards and Certification Manual is available and accessible online at **www.organicfarmers.org.uk/licensees/of-g-control-manual/** (Tel 01939 291 800).

New EU regulations regarding organic wines will apply to the 2012 harvest of UK wines. These new EU laws state that wine bottle labels need to have the EU organic logo on them and the code number of their certification organisation as well as adhering to other wine labelling rules. The new guidelines state production methods and the supplementary ingredients that are allowed. Wine producers wishing to use the EU organic seal cannot use ascorbic acid but can use sulphur dioxide (SO^2) for preservation purposes (but in reduced amounts compared to conventionally made wine). It is possible that the EU will ban the use of SO^2 as a biocide in the future but research into alternative biocide products is currently underway and the EU is expected to release results by the end of 2014. Organic wine can only be made from organic grapes as defined under Regulation 834/2007. Full details of the recent regulations can be found on the following link: **http://ec.europa.eu/enterprise/tbt/tbt_repository/EEC395_EN_1_1.pdf**. Nurseries in the UK do not supply organic grafted vines for planting but the Soil Association conversion time means that by the time the first grapes are ready for picking the vineyard will have gained organic certification.

Organic vineyards in the UK

Meopham Valley Vineyard, Kent, is an organic vineyard where all vineyard practices are carried out by hand and tractor use is kept to a minimum. Currently Dermot Sugrue makes the sparkling wine at Wiston Estate Winery and Ulrich Hoffman at Vivid Wines produces the still wine. No insecticides and herbicides are used on the vineyard and sulphur is used as a fungicide. Weed control is managed by sheep in the winter and mowing in the growing season. The vineyard is managed by Janette Kelly and the main vineyard activity after winter pruning is canopy management in June and July **www.meophamvalleyvineyard.co.uk**.

Other organic vineyards in the UK include:

- Davenport Vineyards, East Sussex
  www.davenportvineyards.co.uk
- Wernddu Organics in Monmouthshire, Wales
  www.wernddu.com

- Quoins Organic Vineyard, Bradford on Avon, near Bath **www.quoinsvineyard.co.uk**
- Albury Organic Vineyard, Surrey Hills **www.alburyvineyard.com** (converting to biodynamic)
- Avonleigh Organic Vineyard, Bradford on Avon, near Bath **www.avonleighorganics.co.uk**
- Avalon Vineyard, Shepton Mallet, Somerset **www.avalonvineyard.co.uk**
- Chevelswarde Vineyard, Chevel House, Lutterworth, Leicestershire **www.facebook.com/ChevelswardeOrganics**
- Bridewell Organic Gardens, Oxfordshire **www.bridewellorganicgardens.co.uk**
- Marden Organic Vineyard, Herbert Hall Wines, Kent **www.herberthall.com**
- Olding Manor, urban vineyard in Lewisham, London **www.oldingmanor.co.uk**
- Pebblebed Wines, Devon **www.pebblebedwines.co.uk**
- Forty Hall Community Organic Vineyard, Enfield, London **www.fortyhallvineyard.org.uk**

Biodynamic grape-growing in the UK

Biodynamic grape-growing and winemaking adheres to the teachings of Austrian Rudolf Steiner, and combines planetary, homeopathic and astrological techniques. Vineyards wishing to grow grapes using biodynamic methods can contact the Biodynamic Association (BDA) which also operates an organic certification scheme **www.biodynamic.org.uk**. The BDA was founded in 1929 to promote biodynamic farming and gardening. The BDA administers the Demeter symbol and gives support through a network of advisers, a journal called Star and Furrow, a news-sheet, conferences, seminars and workshops. The Association's main objectives are to foster and promote the farming method started by Rudolf Steiner in 1924, and to help and support those wishing to put into practice biodynamic farming practises. Membership is open to anybody who is interested, whether or not they are practising farmers or gardeners. The present average subscription rate is £30 per year for members in the UK, £15.00 per year for students and senior citizens. Further details about Demeter can be found on their website **www.demeter.net**. The UK production standards and regulations for the use of Demeter and related trademarks can be found on the BDA website **www.biodynamic.org.uk/fileadmin/user_upload/Documents/Demeter_Standards/2010/Demeter_Production_Standards_-_March_2010_edition.pdf**. There are courses in biodynamic agriculture at the Emerson Campus of the Biodynamic Agricultural College in Forest Row, Sussex. There are long- and short-term courses available, but they do not teach viticulture and oenology **www.bdacollege.org.uk**.

There are currently four vineyards in the UK practising biodynamic techniques: Ancre Hill Estate, Monmouthshire, Wales **www.ancrehillestates.co.uk**; Seddlescombe Organic Vineyard, Robertsbridge, Sussex **www.englishorganicwine.co.uk**; Laverstoke Farm Park, Hampshire **www.laverstokepark.co.uk**; and Springfields Vineyard, East Sussex **www.springfieldsvineyard.co.uk**. The vineyards make their own compost foliar feeds onsite. Ancre Hill Estate adopted biodynamic practices in 2011, but planted the first phase of their vineyard in April 2006. Seddlescombe Vineyard is owned by Roy Cook who inherited ten acres of land near Seddlescombe, East Sussex in 1974. In 1979 Roy started with 2,000 plants on one and a half acres. Today the vineyard has expanded to 23 acres, which includes the vineyard at Bodiam Castle, which converted in 1994, and the vineyard at Spilstead which converted in 2006. Further plantings of the Regent grape variety were carried out in spring 2000, with additional plantings between 2001 and 2003. Now Seddlescombe produces approximately 15,000 bottles of organic English wine per year, and is a member of Worldwide Opportunities on Organic Farms (WWOOF) **www.wwoof.org.uk**. There are a couple of brave producers who are doing experimental "natural winemaking" with minimal intervention during the wine production process, but these wines are not commercially available.

Sustainable grape-growing in the UK

Integrated and sustainable wine production initiatives worldwide focus on reducing environmental impact and protecting resources, but economic and social elements of sustainability are also of considerable importance to producers. The beginning of the UK wine industry's interest in sustainable wine production began with the UKVA Sustainability Group, established in 2009 to explore the development of a sustainability policy and scheme, the adoption of the UKVA's policy of sustainable development, and the selection of sustainability as a theme for the biennial UKVA symposium. Subsequently the WineSkills Sustainability Initiative has produced a voluntary sustainability scheme. This scheme is not accredited and does not provide certification, but it does offer guidelines, online resources and training material. The first full draft of the guidelines was launched in November 2011 on the WineSkills website **www.wineskills.co.uk**, covering the following topics:

Vinegrowing	Winemaking	Business management
Crop management	Energy management	People management
Vine nutrition	Greenhouse gas management	Social responsibility and engagement
Integrated pest management	Water use	
Conservation, biodiversity & ecosystem management	Waste management	
	Traceability and quality assurance	

Sustainability information provided by Alistair Nesbitt, Wineskills

Guidelines for these topics are in three categories: a) Best practice, b) Minimum standards, and c) Proscribed. Producers are encouraged to comply with the guidelines and improve their activities to achieve the best-practice status. The guidelines are reviewed by a Technical Committee on an annual basis. The guidelines are purely voluntary and are a good practice tool, but are in no way prescriptive or mandatory. The UKVA has recently published a report identifying and benchmarking current practice in environmental, economic and social sustainability for English wine producers. The report provides a snapshot of opinions and practices in the UK wine production industry, and makes recommendations for further improvement. The findings of the report will help in the future development of the sustainability scheme. Further information about the UKVA sustainability group, its policy and the benchmarking report can be found on the UKVA website **www.ukva.org.uk**.

Some UK vineyards such as Pebblebed Vineyard, Devon are members of the environment and wildlife organisation LEAF (Linking the Environment And Farming) **www.leafuk.org**. LEAF is a practical organisation that helps with farm audits to identify the best way to increase biodiversity whilst still farming efficiently to maintain a natural balance. Pebblebed Vineyard has left grass strips (beetle banks) around the perimeter of all their vineyards. Pebblebed Vineyard also recycles all their wine bottles after an efficient cleaning process. Bottles are labelled "return to cellar for reuse", and they ask customers to save bottles and cardboard boxes and to return them to the cellar, on the next visit. WRAP (Waste and Resources Action Programme) works with businesses to prevent food and drink waste. By 2015 they aim to reduce carbon dioxide equivalent emissions associated with avoidable food and drink waste by 3.2 million tonnes a year. WRAP can work in partnership with vineyards and wineries to reduce production waste, improve the collection of recycling materials and give advice on recycling organic waste and recovering energy **www.wrap.org.uk**. Further advice and help can be sought from Sustain **www.sustainweb.org**, which is an alliance for better food and farming. Sustain represents about one hundred national public interest organisations working at international, national, regional and local level. It formed when the National Food Alliance and the Sustainable Agriculture Food and Environment (SAFE) Alliance merged. Occasionally there are grants for UK farming and forestry for sustainability, processing and manufacturing efficiency from the Rural Development

Programme for England, Defra **www.defra.gov.uk/rural/rdpe/** and **www.innovateuk.org**.

The Environment Agency

The main aims of the Environment Agency are to protect and improve the environment, and promote sustainable development. They play a central role in delivering the environmental priorities and policies of central government and the Welsh Government. UK grape growers must adhere to certain environmental regulations, including the burning of vine pruning cuttings. Although some vineyards simply leave pruning cuttings in the vineyard, this practice allows for the transmission and overwintering of some pests and diseases. All UK vineyard-owners burning pruning cuttings must have registered an exemption with the Environment Agency. Vineyards that registered before 6th April 2010 will have registered a Paragraph 30 exemption. The exemption system changed in April 2010 so anybody registering an exemption after that needs to register a D7, which is a "Burning waste in the open" exemption. The details for this can be found on the following link. **www.environmentagency.gov.uk/static/documents/Business/D7_Burning_waste_in_the_open_-_ag.pdf**.

For those pulverising pruning cuttings in the vineyard, a T6 exemption is required. If vineyards spread green compost (to PAS 100 standards) under vines, the person who actually does the spreading needs to register an Agricultural Waste Exemption. The T23 exemption covers the composting of plant matter, but spreading should be carried out under either a U10 exemption or a standard rules permit, unless the compost has reached end of waste status. Any animal manure that has a natural plant-based bedding material in it (straw, hemp or sawdust) is not waste when spread on land as a fertiliser, even if it has been imported onto the farm. Further guidance for these waste management practices can be sought from the Environment Agency **www.environmentagency.gov.uk** website or the UKVA.

Single Payment Scheme (SPS)

UK vineyards (not residential gardens) can also apply for the Single Payment Scheme (SPS). Application is conditional on how the land is managed and whether the land management of the vineyard complies with the cross compliance regulations found on the Defra website. **http://rpa.defra.gov.uk/rpa/index.nsf/293a8949ec0ba26d-80256f65003bc4f7/6eb355ea8482ea61802573b1003d2469!OpenDocument**. SPS is part of the Common Agricultural Policy (CAP) and is the principal agricultural subsidy scheme in the EU. Payments are not linked to production, and environmentally friendly farming practices (known as cross compliance) are acknowledged. The scheme is managed by the Rural Payments Agency (RPA) **http://rpa.defra.gov.uk/rpa/index.nsf/home**, and the payment window for the SPS runs from 1st December of the scheme year to 30th June of the following year. There is a cross compliance self-assessment tool on the Business Link website (in the Farming section) which allows vineyard owners to check the requirements and whether their vineyard qualifies for SPS **www.businesslink.gov.uk**. There is a Single Payment Scheme Handbook for England, with details of the scheme on the Rural Payments Agency website including information about eligibility and how to claim the subsidy **www.rpa.defra.gov.uk**. Any eligible UK vineyard who wishes to claim the subsidy must hold enough entitlements to cover the land. One entitlement covers one hectare of eligible land. If you wish to buy entitlements you need to contact the Customer Service Centre (Tel 0845 603 7777, Mon-Fri 8.30am-5.00pm). You need to register your business and obtain a Single Business Identifier (SBI) before any entitlements can be transferred to you from the seller. The person who transfers their entitlements to you (the Transferor) will need to complete an RLE1 form and return it to the Rural Payments Agency by the deadline stated to claim SPS for the coming year. It is important to remember that the minimum amount of land that can be claimed for in the scheme is one hectare.

Environmental Stewardship scheme (ES)

If a UK vineyard (not a residential garden) is registered on the Rural Land Register (RLR), then it may be eligible for the Environmental Stewardship schemes managed by Natural England on behalf of Defra, as part of the Rural Development Programme for England. It is available to farmers and land managers in England.

Case study: Will Davenport, Davenport Wines, East Sussex: The challenges of growing grapes organically in the UK

Growing grapes in the UK climate will never be easy. The relatively high rainfall and cool temperatures, as well as the unpredictable weather pattern, are things all UK vineyards learn to cope with. Restrict yourself to organic methods and the challenges just increase. The key differences between organic and non-organic vineyard management can broadly be divided into three areas, each equally vital to success:

1. Weeds need to be controlled in the vineyard, especially if the vines are young. While the rows can be mowed, the area under the vines needs a more labour-intensive solution. There are numerous choices involved in how to deal with this task, including compost or fabric mulches, strimmers, tractor-mounted cultivating machines, or flame weeders. Each option has its good and bad points but none provide the perfect answer. Apart from fabric mulches, all choices lead to an increase of man-hours in the vineyard over the summer, and this is one of the main extra costs in an organic vineyard. Do not expect perfectly clean weed-free strips in an organic vineyard!
2. The wide array of agro-chemicals used in vineyards is reduced to sulphur and copper for organic growers. There are other permitted inputs, such as biodynamic preparations, potassium bicarbonate and plant extracts, but the spray programme for an organic vineyard will be much simpler (and cheaper) than a non-organic vineyard. It is also less effective at controlling mildew and so it is important to practice good canopy management and regularly check the vines. Unlike some fungicides, sulphur and copper are not systemic. It is absolutely essential therefore to maintain a good spray programme and not extend the interval between sprays or miss a spray when you go on holiday. Any disease outbreak is very hard to control, usually by removing any infected material from the site. Organic disease control relies on prevention rather than cure, and also on keeping the vines healthy by maintaining good soil. Some air movement around the vines can be a useful tool in reducing humidity and disease pressures. Consider this when deciding vine spacing and the

positioning of windbreaks, to avoid areas where the vines may be too sheltered.

3. The absolute key to successful organic farming is in the soil. Healthy soil will grow healthy plants. The focus is on soil biology as well as the soil chemistry. Modern chemical fertilisers are designed to dissolve rapidly in the soil so that they can be readily taken up by the plant roots. The application of these chemicals leads to sudden changes in soil pH, and this can reduce the populations of soil micro-organisms, made worse by the use of herbicides. All the life in the soil (including plant roots) is inter-dependent and so a depletion of soil bacteria will cause changes higher up the food web. In an organic vineyard soil fertility is maintained by addition of composts and manures which take longer to incorporate into the soil, feeding the soil bacteria rather than directly feeding the vines. A healthy living soil will break down dead plant material and make nutrients available to the vines. Because additions of compost and manure are relatively slow acting, the soil fertility inputs need to be considered some time in advance. Any additions will have an effect over three years, so regular inputs should be added rather than waiting until there is a nutrient deficiency. Green manures are often used to perform a variety of soil improvements. Some are deep rooting, while some fix nitrogen, attract insects or suppress weeds.

Specific points to consider

Choice of grape varieties is important and, while ultimately the choice will depend on the quality and style of wine that you want to make, some claim to have better disease resistance than others. Don't select a variety just for its disease resistance – it has to make good wine as well.

Any plot of land will have to be registered and inspected by an organic certifier for three years before the grapes can be marketed as organic. During this period the grapes or wine can be sold as "in conversion". A newly planted vineyard will crop in the third or fourth year, by which time it will have completed conversion.

Yields on organic vineyards may be slightly lower than in non-organic vineyards. This reduction can be minimised by good disease control and regular maintenance of soil fertility. However, in practice there will often need to be some removal of grapes where mildew gets a foothold and, as maintaining soil fertility is less precise, consistently getting good yields is more difficult.

There are obvious savings in aspects of organic wine production, the main one being the increasing costs of pesticides and fertilisers. However, this is off-set by the additional labour required for weed control and canopy management. Overall the cost of organic grape-growing is likely to be slightly more than non-organic growing.

In the winery organic production differs from non-organic winemaking in only a few aspects, mainly the lower limits for sulphites and the avoidance of certain fining agents. 2012 sees the introduction of EU organic winemaking regulations, setting out minimum EU-wide standards for wineries for the first time. It is yet to be seen how the individual certification bodies in the UK will interpret the new rules. One advantage of the new EU rules is that growers will be allowed to use the term "organic wine" on labels as long as the winery is certified organic (as well as the vineyard). Organic wines will carry a new organic symbol. In the end site, soil type and grape variety will determine the quality of the fruit. These basics have to be right. Choosing to go organic adds another layer to the complex mixture of factors to consider.
www.davenportvineyards.co.uk

ES is a government scheme that makes payments for good stewardship and management of the land to improve the quality of the environment. **http://rpa.defra.gov.uk/rpa/index.nsf/vDocView/FFFDD11D4803F7D580256F72003DD33D?OpenDocument**. There are three levels in the ES scheme: Entry Level Stewardship (ELS) (includes the new uplands strand of ELS - referred to as Uplands ELS), Organic Entry Level Stewardship (OELS) (includes the new uplands strand of OELS - referred to as Uplands) and Higher Level Stewardship. The main objectives of ES are to: conserve wildlife (biodiversity), maintain and enhance the landscape, protect the historic environment, promote public access and understanding of the countryside, protect natural resources, prevent soil erosion and water pollution, and support environmental management of uplands areas. ELS provides a straightforward approach to supporting the good stewardship of the countryside. This is done through simple and effective land management that goes beyond the Single Payment Scheme requirement to maintain land in good agricultural and environmental condition. It is open to all farmers and landowners. OELS is for organic and organic/conventional mixed farming methods, and is open to all farmers registered with an organic certification body that are not in an existing organic aid scheme. HLS involves more intricate types of management, where land managers need advice and support, and agreements are tailored to local circumstances. HLS applications are assessed against specific local targets, and payments are offered when these targets are met. All these schemes are found in more detail, including requirements for eligibility and application information, on the Natural England website, **www.naturalengland.org.uk/ourwork/farming/funding/es/default.aspx**.

Glasshouses and polytunnels

Grapevines can be planted in glasshouses/greenhouses with irrigation and air circulation. Strawberry Hill Vineyard, Gloucestershire **www.strawberryhillvineyard.com** has four glasshouses with four wine grape varieties growing under glass, with a further five varieties grown outdoors. Innovatively they are also producing port-style fortified wine. Merlot, Pinot noir, Chardonnay and Cabernet sauvignon are grown in glasshouses, and Reichensteiner, Schonberger, Siegerrebe, Regent and Rondo in the outdoor vineyard. Further advice and vines for growing in glasshouses can be sought from local nurseries including Grove Nurseries **www.grovesnurseries.co.uk** and Sunnybank Vine Nursery **www.sunnybankvines.co.uk**. Alternatively grapevines can be planted in polytunnels which also requires the installation of an irrigation system. Beenleigh Manor in Devon grows Cabernet sauvignon and Merlot grapevines in polytunnels, and the wine is made at Sharpham Estate Winery, Totnes, Devon. The wine is bottled in 50cl bottles and can be purchased from the Sharpham Estate onsite and online shops. Pests and diseases can also threaten grapevines in glasshouses and polytunnels, particularly the red spider mite. Polytunnels can be purchased online from **www.polytunnels.co.uk** who provide advice on irrigation and installation as well as supplying spare parts. Other polytunnel-suppliers include **www.premierpolytunnels.co.uk** and **www.firsttunnels.co.uk**. You do not usually need planning permission for greenhouses or polytunnels, but there are exceptions that need checking with the local authority. If there is less than 20m between the polytunnels and the road, if the structure is over 3m high (or more than 4m if it has a pitched roof), if your site has a listed building or is in a conservation area, national park, or area of outstanding natural beauty then you will need to seek guidance from the local council authority and may require planning permission **www.firsttunnels.co.uk**. Chatsworth Estate, Derbyshire **www.chatsworth.org** grows grapes in a glasshouse which were sold at Waitrose on Oxford Street in London in September 2011 for a limited period at a cost of £2.99 for a 300g pack. The grapes are the Muscat of Alexandria variety grown in Spain, France, Chile and South Africa. The Hampton Court Palace grapevine (*Vitis vinifera* 'Shiva Grossa' syn: Black Hamburg) was listed in the 2005 Guinness World Records as being the largest grapevine in the world. The vine is grown on the extension method where one vine fills a glasshouse because it was thought in Victorian times that a larger crop was produced this way, **www.hrp.org.uk/HamptonCourtPalace/stories/palacehig lights/TheGreatVine**.

Vineyard record keeping

It is crucial to schedule all vineyard operations and to keep records of all vineyard work carried out, as well as dates of major events like budburst, flowering and weather at those important times. Prior to the vineyard being planted any crop or additions should be recorded; all events including budburst, flowering, fruitset, weather and frost occurrences should be documented for future years. In addition, exact details of spraying must be recorded, with dates, amount, and method of application, calibration details, volume used and number of applications. Details of any assessment of bud fruitfulness, pruning weights, disease symptoms, disease cycles, vine nutrition, crop assessment, canopy management methods/timing, bird protection, berry/cluster ripening datum and harvest weights and ripeness datum must be recorded. There is software available for vineyard record keeping and management from overseas companies such as Crop-Trak, eSKYE Sureharvest and Vingro (Vinsight Software), but to reduce costs vineyards can easily set up their own record-keeping system on Excel spread sheets.

Vineyard weed control

As with many vineyard practices, the weed control method is dependent upon costs, labour, equipment availability and vineyard size. Young grapevines are sensitive to weed and cover crop competition in their early years, so cultivation is used to suppress weed growth, but it is important not to damage vine roots or trunks with equipment or chemicals. Cultivation is often used in the first few years of planting a vineyard by using hoeing, rotary tillers (on loose soil) or cultivators around the vines and between the rows, which is best performed when weeds are small. Flails can damage vine trunks which can cause an increased risk of vine disease from pathogens, but disks and mowers can be used between rows. Some UK companies supply this equipment, including Richard Burton Specialised Machinery **www.rbsm.me.uk** and Vitifruit Equipment **www.vitifruitequipment.co.uk**. New and used equipment can be purchased from suppliers in farming magazines such as Farmers Weekly **www.fwi.co.uk**. Cover crops can decrease weeds in between rows, and can even be used as a second crop as long as the crop chosen does not compete with the vines for nutrients. Trials into the most suitable cover crops for UK soils and climate are currently underway. Organic mulches such as straw, green waste or pulverised pruning cuttings, as well as synthetic mulches of polyethylene or polyester, can be used to suppress weeds but must be laid down when the soil is weed-free. Woven fabrics from abroad, that reflect the light back into the canopy while allowing water through, have recently been trialled in several UK vineyards. Herbicides are the main weed-control method used in the UK, and permitted herbicides can be found in the UKVA pesticide booklet online which is also issued free to all UKVA members every February **www.ukva.org.uk/index.php?option=com_content&view=article&id=53&Itemid=62**.

Further legislation and guidance for all herbicide use can be found in the code of practice for all professional users of plant protection products in England and Wales in respect of Part III of the Food and Environment Protection Act 1985 (FEPA), and the regulations controlling pesticides, particularly plant protection products, under that part of the Act. The Health and Safety Executive website has advice, guidance, regulations and the full code of practice available online at the following link: **www.pesticides.gov.uk/guidance/industries/pesticides/topics/using-pesticides/codes-of-practice/code-of-practice-for-using-plant-protection-products.htm**. The non-selective herbicide glyphosate can control broadleaf weeds when they appear, but should not be used near young vines, and care should be taken not to damage the leaves or shoots of vines with spray drift. The UK has a limited range of contact and residual herbicides available for use on grapevines, even though some herbicides have been approved for other crops. Flaming is used in some countries to control weeds in established vineyards, but is only effective on young weeds and should not be carried out near young vines. It is not commonplace in the UK, as it carries risks if vineyard workers are inexperienced, because it can ignite dry mulches or nearby vegetation, thereby starting a fire!

Frost protection

Vineyard site selection is the most effective way of preventing spring frost damage, but do not use thick hedges or solid fences as vineyard windbreaks. Late spur pruning can delay budburst, and leaving extra canes on the vine at pruning means they can be used if frost damage occurs on the other canes. Training the vines high can lift the buds out of the risk of ground frost. Agricultural fleeces are being trialled in the UK by several smaller vineyards to protect vines, and these can be purchased from **www.wmjames.co.uk** and **www.fleximas.co.uk**, as well as some garden centres. These fleeces protect the vines from frosts to -2.5°C but do not offer protection below that temperature and can be difficult to keep in place. Frost protection equipment including alarms can be purchased from N.P. Seymour **www.npseymour.co.uk**. Grapevines can also be sprayed with a polymer coating containing Chitosan and Chitin, a natural alternative that triggers the defensive mechanisms in plants and is sold in some nurseries and garden centres as well as online **www.travena.co.uk/softguard.htm**. Permanent fans can be installed in the vineyard, but these can be noisy for your neighbours. Alternatively fans can be tractor-mounted, but this requires a qualified tractor driver available during the night and early morning and, again, the noise at night can cause issues with neighbours. Oil heaters, agricultural burners, stopgel candles, bougies, smudge pots or braziers are also popular for frost protection, but some of these produce smoke that can cause problems for nearby properties. Companies like Vitifruit Equipment supply the stopgel candles which cost around £6.80 each (depending on the price of oil) and come on pallets of 180 candles. Freight costs are extra and depend on the quantities ordered **www.stopgel.fr/accueil_anglais.htm**. These candles require staff to be available at unsociable hours to ignite and extinguish them, which is worthwhile if it prevents crop damage and loss. It is far better to have many smaller heaters in the vineyard than a couple of large ones, in order to heat the vineyard evenly. Albury Organic Vineyard, Surrey Hills, has converted an old corn-drying machine to continually suck in cold air at ground level and send it skywards. This should create enough air movement in the lowest part of the vineyard to fight off the worst frosts. It is used with other frost-prevention equipment which includes a FrostGuard machine, which blasts warm air around the vineyard, and hundreds of bougies (paraffin heaters) which they put in the rows near to the vines. Vitifruit Equipment also supply an electric cable anti-frost system (central heating for vines) which is expensive to install but worth considering for a large commercial vineyard as it is automatic and cheap to run **www.vitifruitequipment.co.uk**. Alternatively an over vine water-sprinkling system can be installed that freezes the young shoots, ensuring they do not fall below 0°C. Waste water from the winery could be recycled for an over vine frost-protection system.

Weather monitoring

The specific climate of a vineyard site will influence its triumph or assist in its failure. Therefore monitoring weather in a vineyard enables vineyard managers to make decisions regarding spray timing and frost protection, as well as save money and time, and improve grape quality and final yield. Weather stations mainly monitor air temperature, relative humidity, wind and rainfall. Hush Heath Vineyards, Kent, have weather stations installed that send SMS alerts to mobile phones to warn of disease incidence such as Powdery mildew and Downy mildew. This means the vineyard can fight specific diseases with targeted sprays, resulting in less spraying. Some UK companies that sell weather stations include **www.weathershop.co.uk** and **www.weatherstations.co.uk**, and Weatherquest Ltd **www.weatherquest.co.uk** offers web-based weather forecasts for farms. Historical vineyard weather records, especially at key points in the growing season such as budburst and flowering, should be included in the vineyard records.

Common vine yard diseases in the UK

There are many vineyard diseases and pests, but the main diseases that affect grapevines in the UK are Powdery mildew, Downy mildew and *Botrytis cinerea*, whilst other diseases such as *Eutypia dieback*, Phomopsis and Esca are rare. As with every wine region in the world, grapevine trunk disease has become more recognisable and widespread. Ickworth Vineyard in Suffolk, Pebblebed Vineyard in

Devon and Daws Hill Vineyard in Buckinghamshire have rose bushes at the end of their vine rows for early warning signs of mildew, but the type of mildew roses suffer from is different to grapevine mildew. However, they still look attractive in a vineyard, and enhance vineyard biodiversity! Most vineyards use a preventative spraying programme, including organic growers who use a permitted sulphur and copper spray. Noble rot produces dessert wines, but grey rot causes rotten fruit which decreases the final wine quality. *Botrytis cinerea* fungal disease attacks all parts of the vine all year round but is more predominant when it rains near to harvest and at >90% humidity. It attacks flowers during pollination and is especially problematic when grapes are ripening, so fungicides are sprayed. Canopy management is especially important to let the air flow into the fruit zone, and choosing clones with looser bunches is recommended. Powdery mildew is a fungal disease that likes warm, shady, dry conditions and affects fruit set and yield, reduces berry size and colour, and produces a mildew flavour. Downey mildew is a fungal disease that likes warm humid summers. There is a full list of sprays for both these mildews in the UKVA pesticide booklet which is regularly updated and given to UKVA members every February free of charge. Alternatively UK growers can consult the approved list of pesticides and their permitted uses on the government website **www.pesticides.gov.uk/guidance/industries/pesticides/topics/publications/guide-to-pesticides/guide-to-pesticides-contents.htm**. Genetic modification (GM) trials are underway in some countries to insert mildew resistant genes into grapevines, but GM vine stock is not permitted in the UK.

Spraying regulations and qualifications in the UK

Most UK commercial vineyards use air-assisted broadcast sprayers to apply fungicides and herbicides, although tunnel sprayers are used by a couple of the large vineyards. The smaller vineyards use hydraulic sprayers and backpack/knapsack sprayers due to costs of equipment and the size of the vineyard. The label recommendations on the sprays must allow for all these methods, and it is extremely important to follow all the manufacturer's instructions with regards to dosage and timing of application. In the UK it is a legal requirement for people who are spraying with fungicides or pesticides to hold an NPTC (now City & Guilds Land Based Services) pesticides certificate of competence (a spraying certificate or a pesticide licence). Tractor-driving courses are available at land-based colleges and the NPTC website **www.nptc.org.uk** has a list of centres across the country where the PA1, PA3 and PA6 (the main ones needed for UK vineyards) can be taken. Reduced rates can be obtained through WineSkills as well. PA1 is the first introductory course to spraying covering calibration, equipment, safe storage, waste disposal and health and safety. No further pesticide application (PA) qualifications can be taken until it has been passed and no other spray qualifications from any other country are accepted in the UK.

If using pesticides in a vineyard it is important to remember that some plant-protection products have an aquatic buffer zone requirement when applied by horizontal boom or broadcast air-assisted sprayers. If the aquatic buffer zone is to be reduced then it is your legal obligation to carry out and record a Local Environment Risk Assessment for Pesticides (LERAP). For horizontal boom sprayers it is only possible to reduce buffer zones of five metres; buffer zones greater than five metres cannot be reduced. If you just want to apply the buffer zone specified on the label you do not have to carry out a LERAP. However, you are legally obliged to record this decision as is normal in your spray records, as advised in section 6 of the updated Code of Practice for Using Plant Protection Products found on the following link; **www.pesticides.gov.uk/guidance/industries/pesticides/topics/using-pesticides/spray-drift/leraps**. It is a statutory code of practice, which means that it can be given in evidence if you are prosecuted for a breach of pesticide laws. The code gives practical advice on how to use pesticides lawfully. You can also become a member of a professional body, the National Register of Sprayer Operators, run by BASIS, and gain certificates in competence of storage and sale. BASIS is an independent organisation set up at the suggestion of the UK Government in 1978 to establish and assess standards in the pesticide industry relating to storage, transport and competence of staff. The Crop Protection Association (CPA) **www.cropprotection.org.uk** produces a series of guidance leaflets on best practice for pesticide use through the Voluntary Initiative **www.voluntaryinitiative.org.uk**), covering issues such as avoiding drift, emergency procedures and nozzle selection. Other CPA publications include; Keeping residues well within the limits; Working within the pesticide residue limit; Every drop counts – keeping water clean; For the Benefit of Biodiversity; and Integrated Crop Management. It is a legal requirement to keep detailed spray records with dates, amounts, concentration and method of application, and the format of all records should be in place before starting. Further details about record keeping and Control of Substances Hazardous to Health (COSHH) are found on the health and safety executive website **www.hse.gov.uk/coshh**. UK agronomists that can help include Agrii **www.agrii.co.uk** and Hutchinsons **www.hutchinsons-online.co.uk**. Specialist spray equipment can be purchased from Micron sprayers **www.micron.co.uk**, Vitifruit Equipment **www.vitifruitequipment.co.uk** and from new and used suppliers in the Farmers Weekly magazine **www.fwi.co.uk**. Only purchase pesticides/fungicides and insecticides that have been approved for storage and use on grapevines in the UK. Look for the MAFF, MAPP or HSE approval number on the label on the container. Beware of all offers of cheap pesticides, as these may be illegal unapproved products. You can find lists of approved products on the Chemicals Regulation Directorate (CRD) **www.pesticides.gov.uk/guidance/industries/pesticides**. Some organic sprays containing seaweed for plant health have been approved by the organic certification bodies for use on organic crops but you still need to check whether that includes UK grapes destined for wine production. UKVA members are regularly notified of Specific Off-label Approvals (SOLAs) for specific pests or disease such as "Justice" for Powdery mildew and "Option" for Downey mildew. ADAS is an independent, science based environmental and rural consultancy and contracting services to agriculture and the food and drinks industry throughout the UK and internationally **www.adas.co.uk**, and can help UK vineyards. It is also worth checking the Food and Environment Research Agency **www.fera.defra.gov.uk**, particularly with regards to food, drink, plant and environment research in the UK.

Common pests in the UK

Red spiders are more common in glasshouses and polytunnels, but Erineum mites are often visible as blisters on leaves on outdoor grapevines. Wasps are a major problem on thin-skinned and early ripening varieties, and can cause problems for pickers at harvest as well as damaging the crop. Birds are a problem as harvest approaches and there are various ways to deter them. Bird netting is available from **www.birdgard.co.uk** and **www.birdcontrol.co.uk** and can be placed across whole rows, whole blocks or just down the sides of the rows over the fruiting zone. Bird netting is made from UV-resistant polypropylene and lasts up to 10 years, and it is important to get the smaller size hole width to prevent smaller birds from getting in. It can be expensive, due to the added cost of putting on and taking off and the equipment needed i.e. tractor and winder plus the labour required. However, in the long run it can prevent considerable crop loss from birds eating it! Some countries have started using birds of prey to scare birds, but if your vineyard manger does not wish to be trained in handling them then another option is the use of Helikites (balloons filled with helium) that mimic birds of prey. Albury Organic Vineyard, Surrey Hills, uses a kite in the shape of a hawk attached to a 25-m flying line with a 13-m kite pole to protect three to four acres of vineyard from birds. They have also bought a Vigilante Helikite, a shiny balloon filled with helium which flies up to 60m high and will scare birds off the whole of the vineyard **www.allsopp helikites.com**. Other bird-scaring methods include scarecrows, reflective tapes and old compact discs, electronic bird scarers and scare guns. The noise the last two make will probably be unpopular with close neighbours! All bird-scaring methods must adhere to the UK regulations for wildlife control management and control of birds in the UK and these can be found on the Natural England website **www.naturalengland.org.uk/ourwork/regulation/wildlife**.

Rabbits can destroy a vineyard at an amazing speed, so tree guards can be used to protect young shoots: different colours can have different effects but it is best to use ones with ventilation holes. Natural England has a pamphlet available on their website with suggestions on how to prevent rabbit damage to crops other than just using fencing **http://naturalengland.etraderstores.com/NaturalEnglandShop/TIN003**. Organic methods include a natural repellent which has garlic in it, as wild rabbits dislike the smell of garlic and catnip. They are also are not keen on lavender, which could be planted in the vineyard as a rabbit deterrent. The best way to keep deer out of the vineyard is by fencing, but it is expensive to install both for materials and labour. Electric fences are cheaper and easier to install, and can be powered by solar energy if the vineyard is away from a power source. The shock is not lethal to deer but will surprise them! Light brown apple moth (LBAM) was thought to be a new vineyard arrival in the UK, but is now considered a minor threat. Pheasants can be a problem in newly planted young vineyards and those with low bearing fruit, but good deer fencing usually keeps them out. If the vineyard owner has a shooting licence this is an option during the pheasant-shooting season! WineSkills offers master classes on pest and disease management, but it is also advisable to set up an Integrated Pest Management (IPM) system even before planting the vineyard. IPM is used to prevent disease and pest infestation, to monitor infestation and to intercede when necessary with as few chemicals as possible (and no poisons). Vineyard consultants and agronomists such as Agrii **www.agrii.co.uk** can help with the planning and implementation of an IPM programme.

Canopy management and yields

Achieving consistent yields is a major challenge for UK vineyards but we are lucky to be able to learn from other cool climate wine regions. The UK has lower yields than other cool climate regions but these are slowly improving. The most important consideration is to ensure that the basic requirements are in place from the start including good site selection, soil and vine nutrition, soil structure, drainage, pruning (crop load and vigour balance) and canopy management. You need to have viticultural knowledge of what is happening in the soil and the grapevine, and an understanding of the environmental factors that affect them. You can use these facts to make meaningful vineyard decisions safe in the knowledge that you understand how they will affect the grapes and grapevine development. Further important factors

Case study: Hush Heath Vineyards, Kent: Victoria Ash, Assistant Winemaker

The first Vineyard (2002) - Oast House Meadow - 4.14 acres/1.68ha

The first vineyard was planted at Hush Heath in 2002. The site is well protected from the prevailing south-westerly winds as well as from the cold north-east. The soil is Wealden clay over Tunbridge Wells sands, and although it holds its moisture well in dry years, without drainage it can be problematic, especially over the winter and spring, by preventing access to the land and increasing the frost risk. Before planting the vineyard, the rich clay was meticulously subsoiled, breaking up years of compaction, old tree roots were removed and the whole site drained with a network of underground pipes. The vines were hand-planted in the spring of 2002. The rows are orientated towards the south-east, with a row width of 2.30m and 1.30m between each vine, giving a vine density of 3,344 per hectare (1,354/acre). The vines are grown on a vertical shoot positioned (VSP) trellis, with the fruiting wire 80cm from the ground. The vines are pruned to a two-cane horizontal Guyot system (Double Guyot) with an overall trellis height of around 2m. The three classic Champagne varieties of Pinot noir, Chardonnay and Pinot meunier were planted using two clones of each variety and each clone on two different rootstocks. Having different clone and rootstock combinations mitigates to some extent against climatic variation as some clones perform better than others in any given year, and it adds to the complexity of the wine. The varietal mix was selected for the express reason of producing a top-quality rosé sparkling wine. There is, therefore, a slight bias towards the reds: 45 per cent Pinot noir, 45 per cent Chardonnay and 10 per cent Pinot meunier: Pinot noir for fruit, perfume and colour, Chardonnay for finesse and acidity, and Pinot meunier for a little spiciness and je ne sais quoi! This is a fantastically successful vineyard in terms of yield and quality. The 2004 and 2005 vintages were both International Gold Medal and trophy winners, and yields have been amongst the best in the UK.

Small Oast House Meadow (2007) – 0.7 acres/0.3ha
In 2007 a small area of mainly Burgundian clones was planted in an adjoining field. Burgundian clones have smaller bunches and tend towards higher sugars and flavour, with correspondingly lower yields than Champagne clones.

Old 8 Acre Field (2008) - 7.6 acres/3.1ha
May 2008 saw the planting of more vines at Hush Heath. The successful varietal mix and proportions remained the same, though with some new clone and rootstock combinations.

Hush Heath Vineyards at Bourne Farm, Sandhurst (2009) - 9.9 acres/4.0ha
The gradual planned expansion of the Balfour vineyards was continued in 2009 when grapes were planted at nearby Bourne Farm in Sandhurst by the owner, Chris Nicholas. There are two sites, one for the Chardonnay, the other for the reds Pinot noir and Pinot meunier, both being quite steep south-facing slopes. Planting density is slightly higher than at Hush Heath, with a row width of 2.25m and 1.2m between the vines (3,703/ha). The 45/45/10 proportions of the original Hush Heath planting were followed.

Middle Strackney Wood (2011) – 6.52 acres/2.64ha
In 2011 the latest plantings took place at Hush Heath. Middle Strackney Wood was previously an orchard and, as with the other plantings, great attention has been paid to the preparation of the site. In anticipation of planting in May 2011 the site was drained and subsoiled, and had remained fallow for two years. The row orientation has been changed to north-east/south-west due to its narrow shape, giving longer rows (less turning) and to help the drainage of cold air and frost from the site. The Chardonnay, 46 per cent of the vineyard, will be planted at the top of the site, which will be less frost affected. Pinot noir will make up 30 per cent of the area, including some Burgundian clones for colour and flavour. The proportion of Pinot meunier has been increased to 20 per cent, reflecting the results from the winery, which suggest that the grape is rather more

interesting than was previously supposed. Out of interest, 120 of each of the old traditional Champagne varietals Petit meslier, Arbane and Pinot blanc have also been planted (4 per cent). The total vineyard area of all of the Hush Heath vineyards is currently 28.86 acres/11.72ha.

Windbreaks used in the vineyard are hornbeam. Herbicide is used to control the weeds, and there are four full-time workers for the farm (450 acres). Frost protection has not been used in the past but, as the vineyard has been affected by frost for the last two years, they are trialling bougies on the small, frost-prone section of the Oast House Meadow vineyard. They are also leaving the canes standing upright on this section and will only tie down after the frost risk has (hopefully!) passed. A large area of the estate is set aside as a wild area, providing refuge for birds and animals, and encouraging the natural habitat. Pheromone traps are used to monitor pest levels, so that spraying against them is kept to a minimum. Owen Elias has been the Consultant Winemaker for the Balfour Brut Rosé since its inception, and Victoria Ash is the Assistant Winemaker.

www.hushheath.com

include wind shelter, canopy trimming, fruit zone leaf removal and soil management. Vineyard consultant, Duncan Mcniell, FAST LTD explains that "the single most influential contributing factor to lower yields in UK vineyards is lack of heat. The northerly latitude creates growing conditions where less heat is accumulated during the growing season, which results in fruit buds containing on average fewer bunches, and the bunches being of smaller size. The south coast of England is at 51 ° north of the equator, whilst the most southerly wine growing regions in the world lie at around 45 ° south. In addition to this, poor management of soil nutrition levels (especially potash) and excessive soil compaction also appear to be responsible for vineyard soils not maximising their production potential". It is important to remember that soil nutrient levels on their own do not indicate the nutrients available for uptake by the vine. This is because nutrient availability is affected by pH levels, cation exchange capacity and rootstock choice so soil analysis must be carried out in conjunction with leaf or petiole analysis. High sunlight in the canopy will affect plant growth regulators by increasing cytokinin levels but decreasing gibberellin which improves grape quality from the reduced growth of the vegetative parts of the vine. The timing and severity of vineyard practises is important as well as attention to pest and disease control. Chris Foss, Plumpton College feels that "the most common reason for yield fluctuation is cool weather in June, when the vines are flowering. This causes a drop in the sugars produced by photosynthesis, at a time when the vine is steadily growing. The resulting shortfall in carbohydrates will affect the fertilisation of flowers and the setting of fruit, thus reducing the yield for the coming vintage. However, it will also affect the initiation of flowers in the buds that will open the following year, which reduces the number of bunches each shoot will carry in the subsequent spring, so both the next harvest and the following one are affected!" We cannot control UK weather but we can help to minimise the impact of wind and frost occurrences. Some vineyards produce Pinot noir yields of three to four tonnes per acre (70 hl/ha) but yields vary according to grape variety, vineyard practises and weather. Yield prediction techniques prior to harvest are important for winery planning, record keeping and harvest

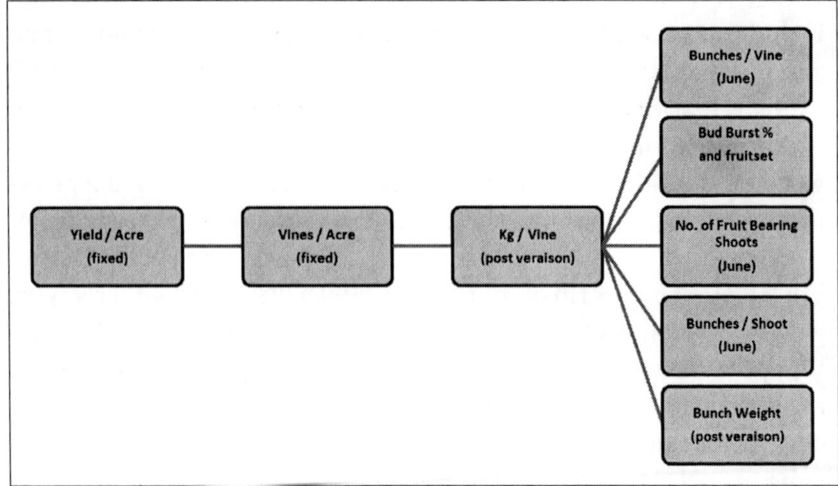

Figure 1. Factors that affect final yield at harvest and data collection should occur (modified from a diagram by Duncan McNiell, FAST Ltd).

organisation. The yield prediction will depend upon several factors shown in the diagram in Figure 1 above.

Good canopy management strategies affect yield and grape quality, and Dr Richard Smart, Author of Sunlight into Wine: A Handbook for Wine Grape Canopy Arrangement, published by Winetitles, Australia, is now resident in the UK and consults for some UK vineyards **www.smartvit.com.au**. Another useful book is Grapes: Crop Production Science in Horticulture, by G. L Creasy, Lincoln University, New Zealand and L. L Creasy, Cornell University, USA. This book covers the influence of the environment on grapevine health and productivity, and is about how grapes are grown and factors that affect grape quality.

Precision viticulture

PDA (Personal Digital Assistants), GPS (Geographical Positioning Systems) and GIS (Geographical Information Systems) can provide vineyard managers with information about the vineyard site, and aerial images can detect differences in grapevine growth. GPS-guided vineyard planting has been carried out in the UK by many vineyards, including recently by Rathfinny Estate, East Sussex, and Greyfriars

Vineyard, Surrey. Other than grapevine planting, very little utilisation of GPS, GIS and PDA technology has taken place in the UK. The size of the vineyard and the costs of technology and equipment are the main reasons for their absence, plus the price point of the final wine. Google Earth pictures of vineyard sites are easy and free but cannot go into detail about soil type, topography and drainage, or produce information to allow growers to match rootstock and variety to soil type, or make viticultural decisions regarding vine vigour. Users need to be trained in the GIS and GPS software and equipment, which increases costs for smaller wineries, particularly as the equipment is expensive. Some university degrees in the UK offer GIS modules within degrees (BSc and FdSc in Viticulture and Oenology at Plumpton College at the University of Brighton) but it is more widely used in agriculture in the UK than viticulture. A remote-sensing PDA is cheaper than GIS, although free GIS software called GRASS can now be downloaded **http://grass.osgeo.org/download**. There has been some research into vineyard site selection in the UK using GIS. Hopefully some UK vineyards will trial more precision viticulture technology tools in the future when costs decrease, and perhaps share equipment amongst vineyards.

Harvest organisation

It is important to have good, clear communication between the winery and the vineyard especially leading up to harvest, whether you are supplying grapes on a contract to a winery or whether the winery is on the vineyard site. While the winery staff are cleaning equipment and ensuring that all the ingredients and laboratory equipment and solutions have arrived, the vineyard and/or winery staff will be monitoring grape ripeness levels. Ideally, the same person should sample the grapes at the same time of day each week and carry out pH, sugar levels (remembering any temperature adjustment that is needed), titratable acidity (TA g/l) and bunch/cluster weights. Acidity, sugar and pH levels required at harvest depend on the wine style being made, vineyard practices and the weather that year. On a commercial scale, vineyard cluster sampling is far better than taking 100 berries from across the block, as it is more representative of the vineyard block. Sample the top and bottom of a slope separately. You will need a pH meter, a thermometer, a hydrometer and a refractometer for sugar levels, and weighing scales. The actual organisation of the grape harvest from purchasing the picking bins and picking secateurs, employing grape-pickers, organising the correct number of pickers on the right days, first-aid training and kits, deciding which varieties will be picked first and, crucially, how the grapes will be transported to the winery, are all important decisions that need arranging in advance. Other harvest considerations include the hire of portable lavatories for pickers, correct size crates that pickers can lift when they are full, wasp sting relief for pickers, removal of tall weeds in the vineyards to facilitate fruit access, paperwork and timesheets/ employee forms for pickers and making sure spraying does not occur before harvest.

The vineyard manager should walk around the vineyard blocks and taste the grapes and check on disease levels as well as agree a harvest timetable with the winery. Late season disease will affect juice and wine quality, and sorting of the fruit to remove affected bunches can be done either in the vineyard by the pickers or on arrival at the winery. The contract winery buying grapes from a vineyard should provide a couple of days' warning of the day of harvest. Weather monitoring is of utmost importance at this time as heavy rain will dilute the berries and can cause splitting, as well as resulting in muddy vineyards where trucks, cars and trailers can get stuck. Health and safety is important, and all staff should be briefed on the company procedures in case of an accident as well as where the accident book is kept and relevant paperwork. Keep records of the yield and picking date per block, of each variety per acre/hectare as well as harvest ripeness levels including acidity, sugar and pH level. These can be useful in future years to estimate harvest dates, but cannot actually be used to set future picking dates. Further information that should be collected includes average cluster weight and total yield per variety and per block, which can be done either in the vineyard or the fruit can be weighed upon arrival at the winery. Harvest record keeping is also a legal requirement in the UK and is essential for the Wines Standards branch of the Food Standards Agency; their forms are available from their website and on the members section of the UKVA website **www.food.gov.uk/aboutus/publications/winestandardsresources**. Vineyards that do not make wine will need to complete a WSB 12 Harvest Declaration, including the continuation sheet WSB 15 Commercial Accompanying Document. Wine producers may also need the following: WSB10 Notification of Enrichment, WSB 14 Deacidification of Wine and WSB 15 Commercial Accompanying Document, WSB 20 Winery Record (optional use), and WSB 21 and 21B Production Declaration. WSB 13 Vineyard Register form is for new vineyards, but sections 2 and 3 must be completed if any changes have been made to the vineyard area. The regional Wine Standards Board representatives can also supply hard copies of the forms.

The UK agricultural minimum wage rates came into force in October 2011 and can be found on the Defra website, including minimum rates for workers in Grades 1–6 **http://archive.defra.gov.uk/foodfarm/farmmanage/working/agwages/documents/awo11.pdf**. The Guide for Workers and Employers, that has definitions of worker categories, sick pay and working time regulations can be found online at the following link
http://archive.defra.gov.uk/foodfarm/farmmanage/working/agwages/documents/awo-guidance11.pdf.

Legal advice

Legal assistance is available for UK winegrowers from APP Wine Law **www.appwinelaw.com**. They advise and assist in relation to UK and EU laws and regulations governing the production, labelling and marketing of wine, the sale and distribution of wine in the UK and abroad, mail order and online selling, and conditions of sale and supply; also agreements with commercial agents, distributors and joint venture partners for the UK and abroad, supply agreements with retailers (including the Groceries Supply Code of Practice), bottling contracts (and other wine-related commercial agreements and documents), and protection and licensing of intellectual property rights in relation to wine products and brands.

Chapter Four

Winemaking

Case Studies

Winemaking

What will you do with your grapes?

Once you have your vineyard planted or your supply of grapes secured you will need to think about where and how you are going to make your wine. There are many factors to consider, not least the wine style you want to end up with. Sparkling wine and still wine have very different winemaking equipment needs, with red wine having different requirements to white or rosé. Even when it comes to harvesting, sparkling grapes are usually harvested later than the still varieties, though there are exceptions to every rule.

You will need to think about the total tonnage of each variety you will reasonably expect to harvest each year. Will they be ready at the same time? Can they be processed together or do you want to make separate lots from each batch and bottle them separately or blend together? These decisions will impact on what size press you will need and what size tanks you will use for fermentation and subsequent blending.

If you have bought an existing vineyard you will be constrained by the varieties planted already. Similarly, if you have planted your own vineyard it will be several years before you will be making wine from the vines. You will be restricted on final wine style by the choices you made a long time in advance.

Becoming a licensed wine producer

If you intend to sell any of your wine, commercially or otherwise, you will need to be licensed as a Wine Producer. This means that any wine you produce will be subject to duty at the prevailing rate. If you are only producing for personal consumption, and do not intend to sell or trade the wine for money or any other consideration (this can be assumed to mean bartering), then you do not need to register and become licensed, and you will not be liable for duty. Producing more than one family can be realistically expected to drink in one year, however, might lead to an investigation by HMRC, so you must keep records that account for all and every bottle produced and where it went. Notice 163 on **www.hmrc.gov.uk** is the guidance for a Licensed

Wine Producer – it is a dry read, but spells out the obligations that go with producing wine.

The duty rates change nearly every year at the Chancellor's Budget, but as of April 2012 the current duty escalator means that wine removed from bonded warehouses will be subject to the following duty charges (on top of which VAT at 20 per cent will also be charged).

Type of wine	£ per bottle (750ml)
Still wine and made-wine: exceeding 5.5% - not exceeding 15% abv	£1.91
Wine and made-wine: exceeding 15% - not exceeding 22% abv	£2.54
Sparkling wine and made-wine: exceeding 5.5% - less than 8.5% abv	£1.85
Sparkling wine and made-wine: 8.5% and above - not exceeding 15% abv	£2.44

Duty on wine and other alcohol is a very lucrative tax for any government and relatively easy to collect, so if you haven't already had a visit from the Excise officers – you will at some point.

If you make wine and sell it commercially you are entitled to keep a certain amount back for domestic consumption by the company (the sole trader, partners or directors of a limited company), employees and guests of the company. The actual amount allowed is determined by the previous year's production, so in your first year of commercial production you will not be entitled to any duty-free product. Once you are established with a track record of one year, the volumes you are allowed to keep for consumption by yourself and your employees is as follows:

A) 5.5 hectolitres (hectolitre = 100 litres) maximum, plus
B) 10% of the production over 5.5hl

A and B must not exceed 11hl in total, and neither can the entitlement be more than the total of the previous year's production. You must record all wine for domestic consumption clearly in your business records before removing the stock from the bonded premises.

Whether you have a vineyard, a winery or both, you will be required to submit either a Harvest Declaration (WSB12) or Production Declaration (WSB21) to the Wine Standards Board by the 15th January of the year following the harvest. This is a declaration of how many tonnes of grapes were produced by each vineyard and the volume of juice extracted. These forms will either be sent to registered vineyards and wineries or they are available on the Wine Standards Board website.

Contract winemaking

You may decide that building your own winery is not a feasible option for you. There are now quite a few contract winemaking operations within the UK for both still and sparkling wines. Most of these are existing wineries with their own vineyards and production who have excess tank capacity that they wish to use to make extra money. More recently one or two wineries have been established with the express purpose of offering contract winemaking facilities. When deciding on the best contract winery for your purposes there are several crucial factors that you must consider:

Location

How far away is the winery? Not only do you have to think about how long it will take to transport the grapes from your vineyard, but what time of day you will be doing the journey. If it takes your pickers all day to harvest a full load you don't want to be setting off from Cornwall at 6pm to get to Kent. The winery will not thank you for turning up at midnight expecting to be unloaded. The alternative is to store the grapes overnight and set off in the morning but, unless the winery can guarantee processing the fruit that day, the grapes could end up having been picked for 24 hours or more before they get into the winery. This can be managed (at least in the UK we don't have to worry about extreme heat at harvest time), but if the grapes are left in the sunshine or out in the vineyard overnight there is a risk of damage from them getting too hot; rain and mild, damp conditions could see rot establishing in the picking crates; and at the other extreme a hard frost could damage the grapes.

Planning transport for large loads of grapes (4 tonnes plus) is difficult, mainly because you won't know exactly when you will be picking until a few days before you do so. You also need to allow a margin of error when calculating how long the pickers will take to harvest the fruit. A good, experienced picker can be expected to pick a maximum of 400kg in a day, but that is assuming a full day with no disruptions. Hauliers will have limited driving times, and if they are hanging around waiting to be loaded this will eat into their working day. You need to make sure you are ready for them when they arrive and get them on their way as fast as possible.

A good contract winemaker will work with you and possibly recommend a reliable haulier who has worked with grapes in the past. They will also give guidance on how the grapes are to be transported and what times they will accept grapes. Smaller loads can be delivered in a self-drive hire truck or on a trailer that you drive to the winery yourself. When hiring a seven-ton truck remember this is not the weight of the load, but combined with the weight of the truck – you can usually get three to four tonnes total weight of grapes/load.

The Wine Standards Board require records to be kept of all grape movements across the country, so they can keep track for labelling regulations. By law, a Commercial Accompanying Document (CAD) has to travel with the grapes – you can download this from the WSB website – Form WSB15.

The winemaker

It is vital that you meet the winemaker who will be responsible for your wines and visit the winery into which you will be entrusting your year's work. Where possible try to taste something that they have made in a similar style to your requirements. It is important that you get on well with the team who will be making your wine – do they have a similar outlook regarding quality?

The winery

When looking for a contract winery it is vital to inspect any that you are considering. How clean is it? What state is the equipment in? Ask to look in the tanks, look at the state of the pumps, hoses and fittings, check out the drains and the state of the floor behind and under the tanks. A well-looked after and clean winery will give you some insight into how careful the winemaking team are in general. If they don't take pride in their working environment it might indicate the care they will take over their winemaking.

How many tanks do they have and are they of a suitable size for your potential crop? If the winery is equipped with lots of large tanks, are they able to offer a truly flexible service. Will the winery have to combine your grapes and juice with others to make up full tanks or do they have the flexibility to make your wine separately from your grapes? It is not unheard of for wineries to take in grapes from lots of small growers, combine them in the tank and then send back proportional amounts from the overall crop. No winery would do this without getting permission from the grower, but it is worth asking if it does happen. And make your views, either way, on this practice known to the winemaker.

The equipment

It doesn't matter how well you get on with the winemaking team or how conveniently close the winery is to your vineyard – if they don't have the equipment necessary to make your preferred style of wine then you have to look elsewhere. For example, if you want your top-quality Bacchus grapes to be made into an aromatic still wine, they will need to be fermented at cool temperatures to retain the fresh, aromatic elements. Therefore, the winery must be able to regulate temperature during fermentation to get these results. Conversely if you want to barrel-ferment Chardonnay or Pinot noir then the winery has to be able to handle barrel work – do they have the equipment for this? Barrel racks, suitable cleaning equipment to maintain the barrels, etc.

If you are aiming for top quality, bottle-fermented sparkling wines the winery will need to have cold stabilisation kit, filtration suitable for sparkling wines, a dedicated area for lees-ageing (preferably temperature-controlled), specialist equipment for riddling and disgorging, labelling, foiling and packaging. Also, how will they bottle your sparkling wine? A lot of sparkling wineries use mobile bottling lines from France, such as those from the Institut Oenologique de Champagne (IOC), which is a cost- and space-effective alternative to maintaining their own bottling line. This does mean that bottling times are restricted to a few days each year – will that timetable suit your needs in terms of ageing your wine? For example, if you plan on only lees-ageing your wine for the minimum nine months, with the aim of releasing it within a year, you will want your wine to be bottled earlier than the mobile lines might be able to schedule. Ask the winemaker how they manage this. They may have capability to bottle small runs by hand.

For still wines the bottling can be even more crucial. For small volumes, a manual bottling line is adequate, in fact you would be hard-pushed to find an automatic bottling line for very small volumes. But if a winery makes both still and sparkling wine on the same site you need to ask some hard questions about bottling. It is not advisable to bottle still wines on the same equipment used for sparkling wines. Although people do, it is such a risk to the quality of the still wines that it is strongly recommend this to be avoided at all costs. Still wines are normally sterile filtered prior to bottling – this is to ensure they are microbiologically stable. Sparkling wines on the other hand are only coarse filtered prior to bottling, because the bottling process, or tirage as it is known, actively introduces and encourages a healthy yeast population, along with sugar and other adjuvants, into the bottle.

If a still wine goes into bottle with any residual sugar (either remaining from the fermentation or introduced to make a medium or sweet style) and comes into contact with yeast, there is a risk that a second fermentation will start in the bottle. Not only is this a quality issue - the wine is not supposed to be sparkling - but also a safety one. Normal wine bottles are not designed to withstand the pressure of a second fermentation and there is a chance that they will explode. Even if you discover the problem before the wines are sent out to market, the cost implication of emptying each bottle, re-filtering and re-bottling with new bottles is massive. There might also be a legal issue with excessive alcohol through the extra sugar having fermented.

Flexibility

It is worth asking if the winery will undertake parts of the process on your behalf. This is particularly relevant to sparkling wine. You might decide to invest in a riddling and disgorging line on your own premises, especially if you have ample storage suitable for your sparkling wine. Some wineries will insist on all stages of the processes being undertaken as part of the process, whilst others will be more amenable. Likewise, you may be able to make and bottle the wine but not have the space or capital to invest in the final stage. Contract disgorging is riddled with potential problems. The winemaker has no idea of the history of the wine and how well the tirage and secondary fermentation went. Upon disgorging he or she might find an insufficiency or surfeit of pressure, causing excessive loss of wine. The wine might be unstable and cause the wine to foam too much to allow disgorging to take place. Be prepared for the winery rejecting a disgorging contract if they feel they won't be able to do it properly. It happens. And the client is left with having to pay again to collect wine that is no closer to being saleable. This is not the fault of the contract winemaker – it will be the fault of the initial winemaker, i.e. you.

Record-keeping

By law all wineries have to keep strict records of where the grapes come from, the weight received, the yield of juice extracted, and the number of bottles produced. See later in this chapter for more details about exactly what and how this should be recorded. Ask the winemaker how they maintain these records, and if possible ask to see a historical record. It doesn't have to be computerised (few wineries in the UK are fully computerised when it comes to their records), but they do have to adhere to the Wine Standards Board requirements.

The same applies to traceability and quality control. Each wine should have full records of all inputs of additives such as yeast, sugar, nutrient, etc, along with lot numbers and rates of addition. If you are ever in the unfortunate position of having to do a product recall, the first thing you will need to provide to the authorities is a full traceability report – make sure that the winery can back you up with this.

The Wine Standards Board provides a template winery record

(WSB20) that all wineries should use – however, for contract winemaking, with grapes coming in from all over and possibly being blended, this form is not fit for purpose. Many wineries use it for guidance, but maintain their own system either on paper or with specialist winery software.

Insurance

Having your own insurance against loss through accident or negligence is vital when undergoing contract winemaking. The winery itself should have their own insurance to cover such eventualities, but it will be limited. If you want to insure for the final value of your wine, rather than just the cost, that will remain your responsibility. Accidents do happen in wineries: it is inevitable at some point that a tank valve will fail, the press could break down with your grapes inside, or the bottling line could malfunction. It won't necessarily be anyone's fault, but the outcome can be financially disastrous, especially for a small producer who has limited stock in the first instance.

VAT on winemaking services

Services supplied within a tax or bonded warehouse can be taxed at the standard 20 per cent VAT rate or they can be zero-rated if the customer prefers (e.g. if they are not VAT-registered), provided the services are in relation to making a new product – this applies to winemaking: the initial product, grapes, becomes a completely different product whilst in the tax warehouse (the winery) so VAT never becomes liable. The customer needs to supply the contract winemaker (or tax warehousekeeper) with a certificate requesting this zero-rating, and any invoices must show VAT applied to the services as 'zero-rated'. For full details see Notice 702/10 at **www.hmrc.gov.uk**.

Making your final choice

Once you have shortlisted your contract wineries of choice you could ask for testimonials from other happy clients. The UK wine industry is small and tight-knit, there are very few secrets amongst us all! The winery should be able to provide contact details of existing clients who can vouch for the service they have received.

Some wineries offering contract winemaking services

- **Three Choirs Vineyard Estate**
  Newent, Gloucestershire, GL18 1LS, Tel 01531 890 223
  www.three-choirs-vineyard.co.uk
- **Stanlake Park**, Twyford, Berkshire, RG10 0BN
  Tel 0118 934 0176
  www.stanlakepark.com
  Vince Gower, winemaker, **vince@stanlakepark.com**
- **Hattingley Valley Winery**
  Wield Yard, Lower Wield, Alresford, Hampshire, SO24 9RX,
  Tel 01256 389 188
  www.hattingleyvalley.co.uk
- **Wiston Estate Winery**
  North Farm, Washington, West Sussex, RH20 4BB,
  Tel 01903 877 845
  www.wistonestate.co.uk
- **Vivid Wines,**
  Moonhill Farm, Burgess Hill Road, Ansty, RH17 5AH,
  Tel 01444 454 615, info@vivid-wines.com
  www.vivid-wines.com

There are others who do contract winemaking on an ad-hoc basis – if you have a winery nearby it would be worth asking if they would consider taking on a contract client.

Building your own winery

If you decide that you need and/or want your own winery then you need to be prepared for considerable expense. Even if you have an existing building it is unlikely to be ready to receive grapes without some adaptation. There are three crucial elements that will restrict a winery's growth: power, water and drainage. All these elements are expensive to adapt retrospectively so it is worth spending time and

Case study: Hattingley Valley Winery: contract winemaking

Disclaimer – the author is the winemaker at Hattingley Valley Winery!

The site of Hattingley Valley Winery in Lower Wield offered the owner, Simon Robinson, a golden opportunity to develop a state-of-the-art winery for his own production alongside a dedicated contract winemaking operation. Wield Yard is located in the middle of the very rural hamlet of Lower Wield, where planning permission for a light industrial processing plant would be unheard of. But when Simon bought the Yard it was already established as a light industrial site, with several business operating on it. The existing complex was almost entirely demolished, consisting as it did of old poultry farming sheds that had been roughly converted into a carpentry workshop and car repair shop. The refurbishment utilises almost the entire footprint of the site with sympathetically designed buildings in the vernacular style of brick and flint with green oak cladding.

Originally the winery was designed to cater for the Hattingley Valley Vineyard of 18 acres planted to the three classic sparkling varieties, with the remaining units rented out to local businesses. Demand for contract winemaking services soon became very apparent and the winery has expanded into the remaining units to cater for this demand. The first harvest in 2010 saw predominantly contract winemaking alongside a few grapes from their own vineyard. 2011 saw production double, with extra contracts and increased yield from Hattingley's own fruit. Increased demand again in 2012 will see the winery expand further.

The model works very well for a winery with considerable capital to invest upfront. The winery needs a press and tanks and the other infrastructure for its own production. This equipment sits idle for most of the year. It makes sense to get as much revenue from the equipment as possible in the short window of opportunity. The winery has to invest in extra tanks and barrels, and extra members of staff at busy times, but the essential infrastructure costs do not increase proportionally. Obviously this still requires considerable capital investment in advance of needing the full winery capacity for one's own production, and does remove the possibility of renting that space to other businesses in the meantime.

For the client the advantages are also huge. There is no investment in costly equipment or premises. A good contract winemaker will take all the worry and bureaucracy away from the client. The winemaking team is made up of Emma Rice, the Principal Winemaker, an early graduate of the BSc Viticulture & Oenology at Plumpton College, who has international experience in California and Australia as well as experience at Nyetimber Vineyard in Sussex making English sparkling wine. A more recent addition is Jacob Leadley, a recent graduate of the Wine Production course at Plumpton, who is the Associate Winemaker, responsible for the day-to-day operations at the winery. Emma also runs her own wine analysis business from a separate unit on-site, which gives the contract clients access to a fully equipped laboratory. This core winemaking team is supported by Simon Checketts, the Farm Manager for the wider business, and Josh Foster who organises the marketing and events side of the business. At harvest time the winemaking team is augmented with students and recent graduates from the UK and around the world, making it a truly international operation.

In the pipeline are a shop with tasting room, conference facilities and a reception centre – these are facilities that winemaking clients can take advantage of when it comes to marketing their own wines or entertaining their own clients.

Hattingley offers a bespoke service to its clients, allowing them to take their wine to whichever stage suits them best. For example, one of their sparkling wine clients has their own storage facility and riddling and disgorging equipment, so Hattingley takes the grapes, ferments, blends, cold-stabilises, filters and bottles the wine with the yeast culture, before sending it back to the client. Other clients take advantage of the storage facilities and riddling and disgorging on-site, and wait until their wine is ready for sale before removing it. There is a dedicated barrel room for fermentation and ageing in oak, and a temperature-controlled bottle storage area to optimise the second fermentation in bottle. To facilitate the contract growers who are bringing grapes from all over the country, at harvest Hattingley has invested in a cold room into which grapes can be put for storage overnight.

There are two presses: a Coquard 4-tonne Champagne press for whole-bunch pressing of sparkling wine grapes; and a 1.2 tonne Magnum press from Oenoconcept which will happily cope with the smaller loads of sparkling grapes and still wine grapes, either whole-bunch or crushed and de-stemmed. There is equipment to cope with still wines and sparkling right the way through the winemaking process.

The tanks are of varying sizes to cope with the different needs of each client, and are all individually temperature-controlled to allow the winemaker complete control over each fermentation. All the tanks and presses are within reach of the in-line inert gas supply. This means that the team at Hattingley can move wine around the winery with minimal risk of oxidation. The choice of nitrogen or carbon dioxide to flush tanks and hoses from an integral system is possibly unique within the UK.

Sustainability

The whole winery is powered by photovoltaic panels on the roof of the buildings – Hattingley Valley was the first winery in the UK to do this, although one or two others have now followed suit. The winery also uses lighter-weight bottles to reduce the carbon footprint of the production further. In addition, there is a state-of-the-art Bio-Bubble wastewater digestor that processes all the winery wastewater. The result is that the effluent from the winery is treated and only water good enough to drink is actually released from the system.

Hattingley Valley Wines, Wield Yard, Lower Wield, Alresford, Hampshire, SO2 9RX,
Tel 01256 389 188
www.hattingleyvalley.co.uk
Contact: Emma Rice, winemaker@hattingleyvalley.co.uk or Simon Checketts, office@hattingleyvalley.co.uk

money getting these right, using specialist consultants and engineers. You will save money in the long term.

Planning permission for a winery is also something you would be advised to get in place before going ahead with purchasing equipment. If you are only planning on processing your own grapes, grown on your own vineyard, then you are likely to fall under permitted development rights, as the winery will be a necessary extension of your agricultural activity in the vineyard. Like a dairy farm needs to have a dairy to process the milk its cows produce, so you are allowed to have a processing facility for your crop.

Wineries and vineyards are still relatively rare in the UK and some planning authorities will not understand what it is you are doing. You may come up against a planning officer who considers winemaking and a winery as light industrial use rather than agricultural. Making wine is an industrial process, and if you are bringing in grapes from elsewhere and / or offering contract winemaking services to third parties, then you will fall into the light industrial bracket. This is where you might fall foul of the planning regulations

If you come up against objections from your neighbours or the planning committee, you can use the Millington case to fight your corner. The Wroxeter Roman Vineyard was facing objections regarding its winery and visitors to the vineyard. The objections were based on the industrial nature of the operation as well as an increase in visitors to the site. The case was subject to appeal after the vineyard owner was refused permission for his winery, and was sent to the Secretary of State for a final ruling. Although the outcome was not conclusive, it has been used to defend applications for wineries since. Matthew Bernstein of Kenton Vineyard in Devon, who used to be a lawyer, has read and interpreted the legal document for members of the UKVA. His summary is as follows:

"Firstly, technically speaking the Court did not decide that this was agricultural use. The Secretary of State had apparently decided the opposite, i.e. that regardless of the facts of the matter, this could not as a matter of law be agricultural use. The case was actually sent for re-determination by the Secretary of State on the basis that as a matter of law this could be agricultural use. It was then for the

Secretary of State to decide whether it was. The judges made it pretty clear that they thought that he should find it was agricultural use, and he seems to have done so. However, in legal terms this is not so much decisive as very highly suggestive. Regardless of this, it does seem to be the accepted position, and quoting Millington does seem to work."

Once you have established your planning requirements, you need to think about the location of your winery. If you have an existing building then this may be a moot point. But if the existing building is in such a position as to make it impractical as a winery then you may find yourself having to build from scratch elsewhere. A winery needs to have certain services and utilities available, so no matter how pretty your stone barn in the middle of a field may be, if you can't get water, power and drainage out to it, then it is no more than a pretty barn. Laying power cables, phone lines, water, etc, can be very expensive and may require separate planning permissions.

Access

This is a vital element of design that can be overlooked. How will big articulated trucks carrying equipment, bottles, tanks, barrels, etc, get to your winery? What are the country lanes like around you? Often, owner-operated trucks will not want to scratch or damage the roof of their very expensive lorry on low-hanging trees. Are there any low bridges en route to your winery? And once they arrive can they turn around? Will there be room to unload from them? Is there hard-standing outside the winery or is there a risk of them getting stuck in wet weather?

Water

It is often said that it takes ten litres of water to make one litre of wine. This is not far from the truth, although in the UK, where we don't irrigate the vines, the reality is probably closer to seven or eight litres of water to one of wine. Do not underestimate how much water you will need, especially at harvest time. Winemaking is 90 per cent cleaning, and you need water, hot and cold, to do so. Sparkling wineries, when up to full production, will use more throughout the year as the riddling and disgorging schedule runs 12 months of the year.

Water used in a winery should ideally be de-chlorinated. Ordinary tap water CAN be used for cleaning (not ideal practice); however, additions made to the wine should be made with de-chlorinated water. Chlorine is a trigger for the bacteria/fungi 2,4,6-trichloroanisole (TCA), otherwise known as cork taint – you don't need a cork for this to happen! Screw-capped wines that have never seen a cork can and do get contaminated in wineries where hygiene is lax, or where chlorine bleach is found in the cleaning solutions.

Good practice is to have carbon filter cartridges on each tap outlet so mistakes cannot be made. They are easy to access and replace.

On the following page is a table used for a 100,000-litre winery, based on a California still wine operation with modifications for the UK. The figures are huge, but don't be tempted to disbelieve them, and of course, remember that what goes in must come out, which leads us on to drainage and sewerage.

Drainage

This is another element which is often overlooked altogether or not truly understood when planning a winery. There are quite a few wineries in the UK that have a pervading whiff of rotten eggs and other nasties at busy periods. This is because the drainage facilities are inadequate for the size and type of processing plant. Whilst you are using a lot of water, you will also be sending an awful lot of chemical cleaning agents and solid matter from the grapes into the drainage system. If you are in an urban area, mains drainage may well take care of it, especially if you are on an industrial estate, but the Environment Agency will still take an interest, as they will in a more rural area.

Winery wastewater has little or no oxygen, and as such is toxic to plant and water life. It has a high solid content and very low pH because of the acidic nature of grapes, juice and wine. The fermentation process uses up most of the bio-nutrients in the wastewater, leaving it deficient and unable to break down untreated. There are various options for treating the wastewater. One of these, proving quite popular where tourism is a possibility, is the creation of a wetland for wildlife. In Australia, New Zealand and other wine-producing countries, these

Information taken from *Winery Utilities, Planning, Design and Operation* David R. Storm KA/PP 2001

Estimated Annual Water Usage (litres) for a 100,000 litre Winery: 700,000 litres
(11,000 cases wine)

Breakdown of Usage	**litres**
Peak Month	84,000
Peak Month Daily Use	3,230
Peak Month Hourly Use	323
Per/min peak use	5
Per/min average use	

Typical Monthly Water Usage Distribution

Month	**% of annual use**	**Comments**
January	6	general operations
February	9	filtration
March	7	general operations
April	8	bottling
May	8	bottling
June	7	general operations
July	7	general operations
August	7	general operations
September	**10**	**Pre-crush cleaning**
October	**12**	**Harvest operations**
November	**11**	**Harvest operations and post-crush cleaning**
December	8	general operations
Total	100	

Hot Water for Cleaning
Examples

	L/min	**Pressure/bar**	**Temp**	**Usage**
Hot Water Hose Stations	25	3.50	60-70°C	Cleaning equipment/tanks/floor – sporadic usage – peak usage Eg: cleaning a tank with a caustic/rinse/citric acid/rinse cycle would take 840 litres of water (210L of which would be hot)

Cleaning the press might take 1 hour, using 1500 litres of water
Not necessarily all hot water but possible

Bottling line preparation May use 1250 litres per cleaning, maybe twice per day

Water Usage table for 100,000-litre winery

reedbeds and wetlands become tourist attractions in themselves. An alternative is a series of settling tanks that will allow the solids to settle out, with the clear water running out at the end. This is probably the easiest and cheapest to install, but the downside to this system is that it will need to be emptied occasionally, and the water that is released into the storm drains, or water table, may not meet Environment Agency criteria.

The method that is probably the best option for a UK winery, with relatively low maintenance (unlike a reedbed system), is an aerobic digester. A big tank is sunk into the ground below the winery and all run-off, solids, winery waste, sanitary waste and greywater is drained into it. The bacteria in the digester get to work on all of the sewage, consuming the solid matter and releasing water clean enough to be returned to the water table. With a winery being seasonal in operation, the biggest problem is keeping the bacteria fed and healthy during the quiet times.

Wineries usually have a large expanse of roof that can be utilised for rainwater harvesting. This 'greywater' can be treated and used within the winery for cleaning floors and flushing toilets. The water can be treated by ultra violet (UV) to ensure any bacteria are killed. In the UK, unlike California or Australia for example, we are not so restricted on our water use and it is not expensive. However, beware the cost of the treatment and pumping equipment required to re-use rainwater – it might take a few decades to realise any financial saving.

Environment Agency Greywater information:
www.environment-agency.gov.uk/savewater
Create an Oasis with Greywater, Art Ludwig 1994.
Harvesting rainwater for domestic uses: an information Guide, Environment Agency 2003.
Reclaimed Water Systems; Information About Installing, Modifying or Maintaining Reclaimed Water Systems, WRAS Information and Guidance note, August 1999 No. 9-02-04 **www.wras.co.uk**
UK Rainwater Harvesting Association: **www.ukrha.org**

Flooring

Integral to the drainage is the flooring. The floors should ideally have a 3 per cent gradient towards the drains to ensure good water and liquid drainage. Wine is very low in pH and most flooring including concrete will corrode with prolonged contact. Likewise, the popular cleaning chemical, caustic soda, is very high pH and will corrode at the other end of the spectrum. Your decision on flooring is one you will live with for a long time. There are many options and they all have a price tag according to how multi-purpose they are.

Polished, power-floated concrete This is cheap, easy to apply and doesn't require specialist contractors. However, it is corroded by prolonged contact with wine and chemicals, and very slippery when wet (which it will be most of the time), so not good for the health and safety of staff. Concrete is also porous so can be a haven for bacteria – a thin layer of protective coating will not withstand much heavy work before cracking or wearing out.

Epoxy resin This is a relatively cheap and durable flooring with a long curing time of up to 24 hours before it can be used. It is not very resistant to thermal shock, with the resin layer possibly coming away from the base concrete under extremes of temperature. It is relatively innocuous whilst being applied, and can be re-applied whilst the winery is in use if necessary, without detriment to the wine. It is laid in one continuous go, trowelled by hand, so seams are less of an issue, but it can crack under extreme weight (such as forklifts).

PolyurethaneThis is the most versatile flooring and also one of the most expensive, depending on how thick it is laid. It is resistant to thermal shock, resistant to chemical spillage, is easy to clean because it is laid in one go (trowelled on by hand) so has no seams. It cures faster than epoxy (in under 12 hours) and the odour is not detrimental to the wine if it is laid retrospectively.

Both epoxy and polyurethane can have aggregate added to the mix to increase the slip resistance, but this does make them both slightly harder to clean.

Methyl Methacrylate (MMA) There is some debate as to how good this medium is for a winery. It sets very fast (in less than 1 hour in some cases), is resistant to thermal shock and chemicals, is durable and often cheaper than polyurethane. It is used in food-processing plants and in some wine facilities, but there is concern that when it is applied the odours it gives off are damaging to the wine. If you are re-laying an existing winery floor or will be using the winery very shortly after the floor goes down, you will want to avoid MMA. But if you are doing the work long before any grapes or wine are introduced, you could consider it.

Power

The amount of power required for a commercial winery can be a surprise, and most of it will stand idle during the year. However, at harvest, when you are running a press, de-stemmer, crusher, temperature control, pumps, etc, all at the same time, you will soon see the need for what might seem like an excessive power supply. Most of these big consumers of power will need a 20-amp fuse dedicated to them. A 100-amp capacity is not over the top for a commercial winery, but you will need to tailor it to your individual needs.

Most winery equipment is run on three-phase power, with some requiring single phase. French equipment often comes fitted with 4-pin three-phase plugs whilst most UK power points will be 5-pin for three-phase. You can either request your electrician uses 4-pin (if most of your kit will be coming from France) or keep a supply of extension leads and converters to hand.

Wineries are by their very nature wet places, with juice, water, wine all being splashed onto the equipment. It is vital that your power points and plugs are the highest waterproof grade you can afford. Good maintenance of your plugs, power points and electricity supply is mandatory for all businesses in the UK under the Health and Safety at Work Act 1974 (HSWA), and more specifically the Provision and Use of Work Equipment Regulation 1998 (PUWER). You can use a contractor to check your plugs through the Portable Appliance Testing scheme. Even if you do use a contractor and get your PAT certificate annually, you must also regularly check the integrity of your fittings and leads, especially during and after busy periods.

It is impossible to say what level of power your winery will need without knowing the projected level of production. When looking at equipment (it is a good idea to start looking long before you break ground for the winery itself) always make a note of the power needs. This will help you plan your power requirement. Any good electrician will be able to look at the power needs of all the kit you will be running, taking into account how much of it will be run simultaneously, and work out how much power you will need. Most commercial wineries are unlikely to need more than a 100-amps power supply, but think about your potential growth.

Communications

Being a winemaker and vinegrower can be isolating in the best possible way, but your business cannot be an island: you will need internet access, telephones and mobile phone reception. If telephone cables are not already laid to the winery site you will need to get them installed. Likewise, broadband internet connections are not a given in rural areas, and if you are too far from an exchange you might not be able to access mainstream broadband. There are increasingly a few companies offering private broadband access to rural areas via a series of wireless receivers. These can be very good, with far faster speeds than the standard, but are more susceptible to bad weather interfering with the signal and they are generally much more expensive.

If you are going to run your internet sales from the winery, you need to have reliable and fast broadband access. Access to orders from the website and emails from customers must be responded to promptly. You need a back-up option for internet access to ensure you keep on top of this side of things.

However, communications are not just for customers: you will be dealing with suppliers, other vineyards who you might be purchasing grapes from, casual staff, etc. You have to be contactable and be able to contact them. Visitors to the winery/vineyard will need to be able to rouse you from the depths of the cellar or the middle of the vineyard. Having some kind of intercom system linked to your mobile phone means you can get on with your day when expecting deliveries.

Visitors

This topic is covered in much more detail in Chapter 5, but you do need to consider access for your visitors if you are going to welcome the public onto your premises. Health and safety is a consideration. You want to avoid pedestrians and vehicles meeting: make sure that any public access points, such as a shop or tasting room, do not require the pedestrian to navigate across a busy yard with forklifts and tractors driving around. You will also need to factor in space for parking.

Equipment you will need

Grape receival Regardless of your style of wine you will need to be able to unload grapes at the winery. Whether this be by hand (make sure you have enough pairs of hands) or by forklift, you need to have an area just outside the winery, preferably under cover, where you can weigh the grapes. If you are unloading on pallets then you need a weigh scale that can take the weight of a full pallet. A pallet truck that can also weigh is a very useful tool because it can perform more than one job. The alternative is a platform scale that is loaded by forklift.

If you are going to use small crates coming straight from the vineyard, for whole bunch pressing, then consider by whom and how they will be unloaded and transferred into the winery. The Champagne-style picking crates holding nearly 50kg of grapes are not uncommon, but you have to have two people to handle them when full. It is much better to go for 20kg or less, allowing one person to safely handle the crates individually. The crates should ideally be vented on at least two sides and the bottom, so grapes don't sit in their own juice or water whilst waiting to be transferred to the winery. Also, think about where and how you are going to wash the crates. You must be able to wash them immediately after unloading. Sticky grape juice left for more than a couple of hours is more difficult to rinse off. A dedicated crate-washer is the best option (although expensive), but a powerful hose on tarmac or hardstanding can do the job – it will just take longer and you will get much wetter whilst doing it.

Wherever you do the weighing it will need to be a flat surface, preferably under cover with room to manoeuvre around it. You need to maintain the scales and ensure they are calibrated each year. Your winery records and yield of wine will be based on the receival weight. If you are weighing heavy, and then don't get the yield of juice you should from the stated weight, the Wine Standards Board and possibly HMRC's Excise officers will be asking where the missing wine (and therefore duty revenue) has gone.

Forklift types There are three types of forklift: electric, gas and diesel. Which one you choose will be dependent on a number of factors. Will it be working outside in the rain? Will you be working only outside? Will it need to be operated inside the winery? Below are detailed the pros and cons of each type for consideration.

Electric Cons

- Expensive to purchase
- Requires a charging station that takes up space
- Cannot safely be operated in the rain
- If they run out of charge then it can take over eight hours to re-charge

Electric Pros

- Quiet to use
- No emissions or fumes
- Can be used inside safely
- Easy to re-fuel on-site

Gas Cons

- Noisy
- Heavy gas canisters to change
- Must have a spare canister at all times
- Emit fumes so can be smelly inside

Gas Pros

- Cheaper to purchase
- Lower emissions and fumes than diesel
- Can be used inside with ventilation
- Can be used outside in the rain
- If you run out of fuel halfway through a job you can simply replace the canister

Diesel Cons

- Noisy and dirty
- Can't be used safely inside
- High emissions and fumes

Diesel Pros

- Cheaper to purchase
- Easy to re-fuel on-site
- Can be used outside in the rain

Once you have decided which type suits your operation then you need to think about the weight you have to lift and therefore the rated capacity of the forklift. A stillage cage filled with 500 bottles of sparkling wine can weigh close to a ton, whilst a load of grapes will probably not get much above 500kg. How high do you want to lift such a weight? Do you want a side shift for ease of stacking cages, or would a tipping mechanism be better for loading grapes into the press?

If you visit the dealer either to buy or hire a forklift make sure you go armed with the facts about what you will be using it for. Renting a forklift on a long-term contract can be cost-effective, as the maintenance contract will usually be part of the deal. To legally use a forklift, even on your own premises, and particularly any staff using it too, you will need to be certified by a recognised training body. Plumpton College offers three-day forklift courses from Lantra, but other agricultural colleges will also offer these. A cheaper alternative is to hire an instructor to come on-site to your winery and train a small group on the forklift they will be using. For example, in Hampshire there is a local training company offering this service, the Hampshire Training Providers **www.hampshire-training.co.uk**.

Each county will no doubt have similar operations. A quick search on Google will help you locate a provider close to you.

General Note on purchasing winemaking equipment

You will not be able to purchase everything you need within the UK. There are some suppliers who, in theory, can supply the equipment from start to finish of the process, but the choice is very limited. To take advantage of the full range of equipment that is available in the enormous European wine industry you will have to look on the Continent. When you do so don't be solely influenced by price. There is no point saving a couple of thousand euros on a press from an obscure supplier in Slovakia if you then lose the saving in the first harvest when the press breaks down and the are no engineers prepared to travel to the UK to fix it. You could lose your entire harvest if this happens. Servicing is necessary for the equipment and, if you are the only winery in the UK with a certain make of machinery, you will pay through the nose to get a dedicated engineer to come to the UK. Look for suppliers who already have clients in the UK, and take advantage of them coming over to service multiple clients pre-harvest each year.

Equipment fairs such as SITEVI in Montpellier, ViniTech in Bordeaux and SIMEI in Milan are usually held every other year – all have websites that are easily found.

Initial processing equipment

Still red wine

Grapes destined for red wine production have to be de-stemmed and crushed before fermentation can start. Red wine fermentation is carried out on the skins, before pressing, therefore you need to extract the stalks and break the skins open to release the juice. In some warmer regions of the world, whole bunches are used in red wine fermentation, but this is not usually recommended for English red wines where ripeness is marginal – the stalks will be green and impart astringent green character to the resulting wine.

A de-stemmer is essentially a horizontal cylinder with holes along its length. Inside the cylinder are rubber paddles that turn to push the grapes through the cylinder. The grapes fall through the holes and the stems are ejected out of the end of the cylinder. The best-quality machines will allow you to adjust the turning speed of the paddles as well as the speed of the cylinder to allow for berries of different sizes. The berries can then be transferred directly into the fermenting vessel, or passed through a crusher.

Crushing the grapes involves just breaking the skins to allow the juice to be released prior to fermentation. It is a good idea to get your crusher from the same supplier as your de-stemmer, to make sure that the crusher will fit directly under the de-stemmer. Transferring the crushed grapes to the fermentation vessel can be messy: a must-pump is a useful but expensive option unless your production levels are fairly high. Small volumes can be bucketed.

Tanks for red wine production are subtly different to those used for white wines. Because the grapes go into the tanks with skins and pulp, the doors are usually positioned at the very bottom of the tank to allow easier evacuation of the fermented, drained pomace. There can also be a door at a higher position to allow easier racking. You also need to think about how you are going to work the cap. This will determine the type of top you will need on your tank: fixed, open, variable, etc. As the grapes ferment, a cap of skins will form at the top of the tank which needs to be kept wet. This is crucial for several reasons: to prevent the growth of bacteria in the drying out skins; to extract more colour and other phenolics from the grapes; to aerate the fermenting must. There are several ways to do this: ask five winemakers which is the best method and you will get five different answers. It is often related to the grape variety and style of wine: Pinot noir is often punched down, Cabernet sauvignon more often pumped over, with rack and return reserved for wines needing some additional oxygen during fermentation or extra extraction. The three principle ways are:

Punching down (pigeage in French)

This is when you physically, either manually or with a pneumatic device, force the cap back under the fermenting liquid until it is completely wet and submerged.

Pumping over (remontage in French)

This is when you attach a hose and pump to the bottom valve of the tank and pump the liquid out and over the top of the tank, thoroughly wetting the cap.

Rack and return

This is similar to a pump over, with the addition of another vessel or tank being utilised between the tank and the pump returning to the tank to 'splash' the wine, allowing an aerative racking.

Once fermentation of the red wines has finished you will need to drain the wine from the grape pomace. The wine will need to settle for a few days without pump overs or punch downs, possibly with some dry ice sprinkled on to prevent oxidation if in an open-top vat, or just tighten the lid to trap the existing carbon dioxide in the tank if in a closed-top tank. The 'free-run' wine can then be drawn off the bottom valve. This will be the best wine, but there is still a considerable volume within the skins and pulp. This has to be transferred to a press to extract the remaining liquid – a mustpump can be re-used at this stage. Known as the 'press wine' you will need to make a decision as to whether it is of good enough quality to be mixed back with the free-run wine. This will partly depend on the quality of the press you are using and how hard you press the pomace. You may decide to keep it separate and make a lesser wine for your own consumption, or use it as 'topping wine' for your barrels or other vessels where a small percentage won't affect the quality.

Still white wine and sparkling base wines

For still white wines you can crush and de-stem the grapes before transferring them to the press. This means you get more into the press and can process more efficiently and faster. However, for top-quality white wines and certainly for sparkling base wines whole-bunch pressing gives you a lower solid content in the juice. There is a reason that this is the way it is done in Champagne and other quality sparkling wine regions, not just because of tradition. In my experience in California and Australia all the top-quality fruit destined for the higher-end still white wines was pressed as whole bunches. That is not to say that crushing and de-stemming means automatically lower quality, there are many exceptions who prove the rule.

If you are looking at presses and you are quoted for a press size in hectolitres, they are probably talking about crushed, de-stemmed fruit capacity, whereas if you are quoted in terms of the tonnage it will accept then it is more likely based on the weight of whole bunches. Make sure you understand in what terms the supplier is talking about before you commit!

As for types of press there are numerous options, but the most common models are the following.

Basket press

Large versions of these are used in Champagne where Coquard is the ubiquitous supplier. Essentially a large basket made of wooden or stainless steel slats with a juice tray underneath, a hydraulically operated plate is then pressed on to the top of the grapes to force the juice out through the slats into the tray. To ensure an even extraction from the grapes, the pomace needs to be manually shifted in between pressing cycles. This is often called the 'retrousse' and it is a labour intensive operation, with a larger press size adding considerable time to the processing. Coquard has updated the design principle with its new PAI press that operates horizontally, eliminating the need for manual intervention during the pressing cycle. There are many other manufacturers of basket-type presses from across Europe. A visit to one of the many equipment fairs would give you the opportunity to see all the options in one go.

Bladder press or pneumatic press

These presses come in many sizes and variations. The principle of the operation is a stainless steel vat, mounted horizontally, with an air bladder running the length of the vat inside. The air bladder is filled by a compressor, squeezing the grapes against the wall of the vat where grills allow the juice to run out. Variations on this are centrally mounted grills with a bladder either side; open-vat presses where the grills allow the juice to run down the outside of the vat and into the juice tray; or closed-vat presses with internal grills allowing the press to be operated under inert gas, releasing the juice out through channels.

If you are making only sparkling wine then an open-vat press is better – allowing some oxidation of the juice as it runs down the press, but if you are also making still white wines and pressing red wines off you might want to consider a closed-vat press that will allow you to operate the press anaerobically, or under inert gas, to retain primary fruit aromas.

Up to about 4 tonnes (whole bunch weight) a bladder press will come with its own internal air compressor and can also still be mounted on wheels. Any bigger than that and you will probably need an external reservoir of compressed air and a stand-alone compressor. And you will have to fix the press to the floor, making moving it somewhat difficult.

Horizontal screw press

This type of press is going out of fashion and is more often used in large-scale wineries where crushing and de-stemming is the norm. The operation principle is the same as the basket press, but horizontal rather than vertical; it allows for greater volumes to be processed faster than a basket press. It is mostly found in large-scale wineries.

Continuous screw press

These are now almost obsolete and you would probably only find one on the second-hand market. There is a reason for this: the quality of juice is not good. They are rough on the grapes and are actually prohibited in lots of quality wine regions.

Hydro-presses

These are for small-scale winemaking and come in various sizes suitable for home winemaking and smaller commercial wineries. Similar in operation to a pneumatic bladder press, instead of the internal bag being blown up with compressed air the rubber bag inside the press is inflated by filling it with water. The juice then runs out of the stainless steel perforated cylinder.

Some of the manufacturers that supply to the UK already are:

- Magnum de Franceschi by Oeno Concept, Epernay, France **www.oenoconcept.com**
- Bucher Vaslin, across Europe **www.buchervaslin.com**
- Europress, Germany **www.scharfenberger.de**
- Willmes, UK agent, Vigo Ltd **www.vigoltd.com**
- SK Group, UK Agent, David Cowderoy, cowderoy.david@gmail.com **www.sk-group.biz**

Tanks

The size and type of tanks will depend on the size of your vineyard and the parcels within it. If you want to ferment the individual parcels separately, then you will need to get more small tanks, but this will increase the cost per litre of capacity. If the intention is to then blend your wine you will need bigger tanks to do this. Bear in mind the size of your press and the volumes you can expect to extract in one pressing cycle. How close together will the grapes come in? Can you add one pressing to the previous one in the tank before settling begins?

With sparkling wine, if your press will take 4 tonnes of whole bunches you can expect to get 2,000 litres of the best juice for your 'cuvée' and about 500 litres of heavier pressings or 'taille'. Will you be separating these out from one another? With sparkling wine you can generally expect a yield of approximately 50 per cent cuvée and 10 per cent taille, whilst with still wines you could take up to 70 per cent juice from the grapes. So, on 1,000kg, 60 per cent yield would be 600 litres. This is a decision that has to be finalised at the pressing itself, according to the quality of the fruit, the level of rot, the ripeness, etc.

White wine tanks have a door raised above the base of the tank. This allows you a settling space at the bottom for solids and, later, yeast lees from the fermentation. After draining off the bulk of the juice or wine you can open the door to carefully watch the remaining clear liquid off the solids. This is either done by the use of a racking plate, or the tank will be fitted with a racking arm that you control from outside the tank. The latter is the easiest way.

Some of the manufacturers that supply to the UK already are:

- Metalinox, Family owned company from the Loire Valley, dimitri.dupaillon@metalinox-sas.fr
- SK Group, UK Agent, David Cowderoy, cowderoy.david@gmail.com **www.sk-group.biz**
- Speidel, UK agent, Vigo Ltd **www.vigoltd.com**

Valves

The racking valve of a tank should be a ball valve, to allow the insertion of equipment such as rousers or stirrers, whilst the bottom valve should be a butterfly valve for ease of cleaning. The fittings on these valves should all match the other equipment in the winery. DN fittings are the most common in the UK and DN40 is a manageable size. Watch out for secondhand equipment with weird and wonderfully old-fashioned fittings left over from the imperial days. Any savings you make on the kit could be lost by having to commission reducers and converters to fit your other equipment. Macon fittings are ubiquitous throughout Europe, so when ordering new kit from suppliers always specify which type and size fitting you want.

With DN fittings there is always a male and female end. It can be easier to decide that all equipment like tanks and presses and pumps are fitted with male ends whilst all hoses are fitted with female ends. This way you never find yourself with a hose with the wrong fitting. Always useful, however, are a few adaptors such as a male-to-male connector that can join two female hoses together in case extra length is needed.

Temperature control or thermo-regulation

Once your juice has been pressed you will need to settle out any solid matter. This is done either with enzymes or by cold-settling. If you are cold-settling then you need to get the juice below 10°C (if you are using enzymes then these won't work below 12°C). So your tanks need to have individually controlled thermo-regulation or you need to have tanks inside a cold room.

It is far more efficient in the longer term to have tanks that can be individually controlled. Once you have settled the juice for 12-24 hours you will rack it off the solids into another tank and initiate fermentation. For the yeast to start fermenting in ideal conditions the juice should be at no less than 15°C.

Once fermenting the temperature will depend in what style of wine you are making. An aromatic white such as Bacchus might be maintained at 15°C whilst a sparkling base wine, where you are not attempting to retain primary fruit aromas, can be allowed to rise to 20°C or maybe even more. A red wine, being fermented on its skins, will need to be kept warm and allowed to reach 30°C before cooling kicks in.

Once alcoholic fermentation has finished, the wine may need to go through malolactic fermentation, whereby the harsher, green malic acid is converted to softer lactic acid by malolactic bacteria. To enable this conversion, the wine needs to be maintained between 20 and 25°C: any hotter and the bugs will die, cooler and they will go dormant.

When deciding on the extent of your thermo-regulation system you need to consider if you will require heating and cooling at the same time. This adds considerably to the cost, because you effectively need two circuits for the glycol, but also gives you ultimate flexibility.

Two suppliers of dedicated winery thermo-regulation systems found in the UK are:

- Vigo Ltd, sales@vigoltd.com **www.vigoltd.com**
- TR Equipements, philippe@trequipements.fr **www.trequipements.fr**

Chaptalisation and de-acidification – additions to wine

There are certain additions you can make to your juice and/or wine to help nature along its way. In the UK we rarely see sugar levels in the grapes that would allow us to produce wines with a natural alcohol of more than 11-12 per cent. And those wines that do reach the giddy heights of 11 per cent natural alcohol are from grape varieties that are specifically designed to ripen well in cool climates, but they are not necessarily the highest quality grapes.

The classic sparkling varieties of Chardonnay, Pinot noir and Pinot meunier will very seldom achieve more than 10 per cent natural potential alcohol before harvest in October. And they will also retain more acidity than would be acceptable for a still wine. For both still and sparkling wines you are permitted to add (chaptalise) up to 3 per cent potential alcohol to the juice after pressing and before or during the primary fermentation. Potential alcohol in this context is another word for sugar – whether it is the natural grape sugars of fructose and glucose, or sucrose courtesy of Silver Spoon or Tate & Lyle – the result is more potential alcohol in the juice.

In some exceptionally cool years the UKVA can apply to the EU for an extra 0.5 per cent potential alcohol at chaptalisation, bringing the total allowed to 3.5 per cent. The Wine Standards Board regulates the addition of sugar, or 'enrichment' of juice as it is known. There are minimum natural alcohol levels your juice/grapes must reach before enrichment or chaptalisation, and these differ slightly for sparkling and still wines. Essentially, the total potential alcohol level after enrichment must be at least 8.5 per cent, meaning that the absolute minimum level of ripeness of the grapes has to have been 5.5 per cent. The levels are detailed on the Wine Standards Board website where you can also download the official WSB10 Notice of Enrichment form that you are legally obliged to complete and send to your Wine Standards Inspector at least 48 hours before you carry out the enrichment operation.

Whether you measure your sugar by Brix, Baumé, Specific Gravity or Oeschle, you must ensure your conversion rates are accurate enough to satisfy the WSB requirements. For the additions you can assume that just under 17g/l of sugar will translate to 1 per cent potential alcohol. It is not an exact science because the conversion of sugar to ethanol during the fermentation is not always linear.

De-acidification

This is very rarely used on sparkling base wines, despite these having some of the highest acid levels. Thc lees-ageing period for sparkling wines offers an opportunity for softening of the acidity as well as malolactic fermentation. However, for some aromatic still wines where MLF is not an option and the acidity levels are still high, artificial de-acidification is necessary. It is a very violent process and carries great risk of severe oxidation as the pH is significantly raised on a portion of the juice. If you have to do it you should try to do it on juice where possible, rather than wine. The WSB requires notification of any de-acidification operation regardless of when it takes place, and the notification does not have to be received in advance, unlike with enrichment - use Form WSB14.

There are two ways to remove acidity – single salt and double salt. Calcium Carbonate will remove only tartaric acid, so if you have 7g/l total acidity and 5g/l of that is malic acid, if you remove 2g/l of acidity with calcium carbonate you will be left with 5g/l of acidity, but it will be all malic acid and will leave the wine tasting unbalanced. To remove both tartaric and malic acid you need to do a double salt de-acidification. This will remove roughly 1g/l of malic for each g/l of tartaric. So you still need to be aware of the different levels so you don't remove all the tartaric acid. There are several proprietary double salt preparations – each with different actions and instructions. It is best to take advice from the supplier before embarking on any de-acidification.

Cold stabilisation

A vital stage in the process of white and sparkling winemaking. The naturally occurring potassium bitartrate (KHT) as tartaric acid in wine will often precipitate out when the wine is chilled, forming a crystalline substance in the bottle, which can look worryingly like glass. It is not harmful in itself but it is considered a fault, especially by retailers who don't want to have to explain what it is when selling the wine or deal with the complaint when the customer brings it back thinking the crystals are glass.

With sparkling wine the added complication is dealing with tartrate crystals at disgorging. They will act as a nucleation point for foaming and cause you to lose far more wine than is commercially viable.

So, how to prevent this happening? There are a few options and most of them are expensive. First of all, barrel-fermented and aged wines are often naturally cold stable. A combination of being aged on the lees, a greater surface to volume ratio for precipitation in the barrel, and a smaller vessel getting colder during the winter, can contribute to the stability. But do not assume this – get the wine tested before you bottle.

Physical cold-stabilisation by chilling the wine below zero, ideally to -4°C, and holding it there for several weeks can also perform the process naturally. This is impractical for most wineries and is not advised. Doing the same but also adding cream of tartar to act as a seed for the precipitation of tartaric acid is a better solution. There is some debate amongst winemakers about how long you need to keep the wine chilled and in contact with the cream of tartar, and it ranges from a few hours to 48 hours. In theory once the wine hits saturation point it will be stable and any further chilling time will not do anything more. It is only trial and error that will tell how your wines will behave.

It is vital that you cold stabilise your wine as the last process before filtration and bottling. Any other processes or additions such as blending or sweetening can render a previously stable wine unstable. The wine needs to be moving as it is chilled to prevent the liquid from freezing. Our relatively low-alcohol wines in the UK obviously have a higher freezing point than most.

You also need to protect it from oxidation because oxygen is more soluble at low temperatures, making the wine vulnerable at this stage.

Most wineries will have a dedicated cold stabilisation tank that has extra chilling capacity. If you don't have three-phase power in your winery, this operation and these low temperatures could prove quite tricky to achieve. Wrapping the tank in bubble wrap or other insulating material can also help. You can also use a free-standing heat exchange unit that can be hooked up to individual tanks – these circulate the wine whilst chilling, and require a centrifugal pump that will be able to keep the wine moving without freezing up. There is also some concern about how gentle this process is – biodynamic winemaking prohibits the use of centrifugal pumps because of the perceived sheering of the wine as it is circulated.

Other methods are electrodialysis, metatartaric acid or carboxymethylcellulose (CMC). Electrodialysis is quick, irreversible, and uses significantly less power than physical cold stabilisation. However, it requires a specialist machine and, while these are widely available for contract hire in Europe and New World wine regions, there isn't a single one in operation in the UK, as far as I am aware. The machines are too expensive for a winery to consider buying one for their own use.

Metatartaric acid is an additive that can be used at bottling or disgorging to provide temporary stability by inhibiting the precipitation of crystals. It is fine for wines designed to be drunk within a year or so. The effectiveness of the treatment is very much dependent on what temperature the wine will be stored. If kept in a cool cellar at 10°C then it could remain stable for 18 months, whilst at 25°C it may only be a few months.

CMC is a new product for wine, approved for use in the EU only in the last few years. It has, however, been around as a food additive for many years. Its action, like metatartaric acid, is an inhibitory one, but it is more stable. Trials are essential because the CMC can react with certain types of wine leaving them cloudy.

It is worth noting that the last three methods do not significantly reduce the final acidity of a wine, unlike the physical cold stabilisation. In some wine regions this is desirable because natural acidity is low anyway, but in the UK we are often battling high acidity, and the removal of tartaric acid at this stage is a bonus in helping to achieve the right balance in the wine. There are also possible quality issues with the final three methods. Most high-quality wineries use cold stabilisation as the first choice, despite its high cost in terms of power usage and time. Electrodialysis is only really cost-effective in very large-scale production wineries. The use of additives to inhibit crystal formation is often considered a last resort for small batch winemaking and to rectify problems once in bottle (at disgorging for example).

Filtration

Most wines will need to be filtered prior to bottling, unless you are making a natural wine. For still wines it is necessary to ensure they are sterile-filtered to a 0.25 or 0.45 micron level. The numbers refer to the pore size of the filter, and indicate the type of foreign body the filter will remove. 0.25 will remove bacteria whilst 0.45 will remove yeast cells. If you make still wine in a winery where sparkling wine is also made, and you retain some residual sugar in the wine, you will need to sterile filter to avoid unwanted secondary filtration. It is also an aesthetic issue. Most consumers expect their wines to be bright and clear, with no haze.

At bottling, white wines should have a turbidity measurement of no more than 1.5 NTU when measured on a nephelometer. Red wines can be higher but probably no more than 4 or 5 NTU at the most.

To achieve this level of clarity you can choose from several types of filter:

Cross-flow filtration

These machines are very expensive to purchase: there are no mobile contract services in the UK, so at a cost of about 50,000 euros I have discounted this one for the UK market. They are very efficient, but in terms of quality winemaking, especially for sparkling wines, they are still being assessed.

Pad filtration

Very traditional and found all over the world, a plate and frame filter is very versatile and relatively simple to use. The downsides are a risk of paper taste from the pads that are placed in the frames, unless they are flushed through with plenty of water first. There is also the risk that the wine will be watered down by this process, especially with small volumes. The pads themselves are cheap, but they are one use only so, unless you can filter several wines in one go, you need to have plenty of spares. They come in various sizes and you can buy pads to cope with different levels of filtration. A great advantage is that the first pads can be coarse filtration followed by finer filtration in the same movement, saving time and reducing the number of times the wines have to be moved.

Cartridge filtration

These come in many guises and sizes. They are simple to set up and use. A stainless steel housing contains removable cartridges so you can use the same housing for varying levels of filtration. The cartridges themselves can be cleaned and stored for re-use in the same season, though it is not recommended to attempt to keep a cartridge more than one vintage. They are more expensive to buy than the pads, but ease of use and ease of cleaning can out-weigh the cost.

Diatomaceous earth filtration

This is the classic method of filtration for sparkling wines including Champagne. However, DE filtration is rapidly falling out of favour. The earth, a fine powder made up of the microscopic skeletons of long-dead sea creatures (diatoms) is found in the largest quantities in Germany (where it is known as kieselgur), and Nevada and Colorado in the USA.

The earth offers inert filtration, neither imparting nor stripping out flavour. The drawbacks are the potential health risk to operators – breathing in the fine dust, although no longer thought to be carcinogenic, can damage lungs because of the 'sharp' nature of some types of earth. The porosity of the earth can also cause excessive drying of the skin with prolonged contact. A further disadvantage is the filtration machinery. It is made up of lots of moving parts, complicated valves and pumps. A skilled operator is required to get the earth to coat the discs properly and form a good filtration aid. The final disadvantage is disposal of the earth once you have finished with it. It cannot be put down the drains and should not be thrown in the regular rubbish – there is a requirement to have it disposed of properly, which inevitably involves cost.

Lenticular filtration

This is a relatively recent innovation and one that is rapidly replacing DE filtration in Champagne and other quality sparkling wine regions, because it does a very similar job but without the health hazards and disposal problems. The great advantages are no moving parts to the filter: you just need a centrifugal pump (ideally, although a basic impeller will do the job) hooked up between the tank and filter. The filtration medium is a cellulose and is housed within discs negating the need for the operator to handle it. You do need to flush with water to remove any residual taste. The discs can be stored within the filter after use, with SO2 and citric acid to maintain them until the next use. Depending on the size of the winery you could expect to filter an entire vintage through the same discs.

Bottling

The most crucial stage for any winemaker, this is where you can mess up an entire year's worth of wine if you don't get it right. Cleanliness and oxygen are the two most important factors for all all types of wine, but most particularly still wines. As soon as a wine is bottled it starts on its path to vinegar. Any bacteria in the wine, or introduced at bottling, along with excess oxygen will speed up this process. You want to ensure the consumer opens the same wine you intended when you made it.

A lot of the sparkling wineries in the UK utilise the mobile bottling lines of the Institut Oenologique de Champagne (IOC). This takes out the need for a dedicated area within the winery. Also, as sparkling wines are going to be destined for a few years lees-ageing they can all be done in one go. The fast lines (up to 5,500 bottles per hour) are more efficient than most UK wineries could ever hope to justify owning, so the bottling is done in a few of days. There is enough equipment in a winery that is only used for a few weeks of the year: there is no need to add a bottling line to this list.

Still wine bottling will have to be done on-site or shipped out in bulk and bottled under contract in another winery who does this (such as Bolney Wine Estate in West Sussex), or a specialist contractor as used by the supermarkets and bulk shippers of wine. The volumes required to make this viable are considerable and beyond the majority of UK wineries.

Manual bottling is a necessary evil for most small-scale wineries in the UK. Automatic bottling lines are expensive and require a certain volume to work efficiently. Manual bottling carries a high risk of oxygen uptake. If you can flush the bottles with inert gas such as nitrogen or argon before filling, you will have an advantage. Do not use carbon dioxide at this stage: the CO2 will dissolve into the liquid and you will end up with an unintended spritz to the finished wine. Measuring the Dissolved CO2 of your wine is recommended, and you can adjust according to style: white wines should be in the region of 1200 to 1500 mg/l DCO2 at bottling – if it is excessive you can sparge the wine in the tank with nitrogen to remove the CO2. Red wines are usually bottled between 600-800mg/l.

Similarly you can measure the Dissolved Oxygen (DO2) in the tank before bottling. It should be below 1-1.5mg/l - sparge with nitrogen to remove an excess. It is also advisable to then check the DO2 again in the bottles – if the pick-up of O2 is greater than 1mg/l you have a problem on the line and need to stop, tighten all the fittings, use nitrogen gas to sparge the bottles, etc.

Checking the fill-height as you proceed with bottling is also necessary, and legally you are obliged to do so and record your measurements. There are many types of still wine bottle and the standard 750ml size, whatever shape, will have a figure on the bottom indicating how many millimetres from the top the wine level should be at. It is usually somewhere between 63 and 73mm: measure with a ruler to ensure that Trading Standards will be happy with the consistency of your filling. It is better to be slightly over than under, but you can be penalised either way.

Cleaning your bottling line

Everything must be squeaky clean prior to bottling, and steam is the easiest and most efficient way to do this. You can use a combination of hot water, caustic soda and citric acid if steam is not available, but you need to be very thorough. Steam is absolutely vital if you are bottling still and sparkling wines on the same line. Yeast cells, deliberately introduced into the sparkling bottles, can hibernate and survive from one season to the next. Steam is the only reliable cleaning method that will get into all the nooks and crannies of a bottling line.

If you are lucky enough to be able to justify and afford an automatic bottling line you need to consider the following before purchase:

Speed How many bottles per hour? Can you keep up? Will it do your small volumes as well?

Closures Can you choose screw-cap, cork, crown cap – interchange between all three or only one?

Inert gas Can you flush the bottles with gas automatically?

Bottle type Can you use burgundy, bordeaux and sparkling bottles? Half-bottles, magnums? How adjustable is the line?

Labels Will it fit the type of labels you want? It is easier and cheaper to fit labels to the line rather than vice versa, but you need to make sure the line is compatible, especially if you have an odd-shaped design.

Labour How many people are required to operate the line efficiently? Would it be worth spending money on conveyors and turntables in the line to reduce the number of people required.

Analysis

Trying to make wine without any kind of analysis is like trying to drive blindfolded. You can do it and you might be alright but the chances of an accident are hugely increased. Some of the basic analysis kit can be purchased quite reasonably, and being able to check certain parameters on site can speed up decision-making at all stages. There are two laboratories in the UK offering dedicated wine analysis (see below) for wine producers. The cost of testing a sample for a 500-litre batch of wine is the same as it is for a 5,000-litre batch, so costs do rise exponentially, but knowledge is power, and if you can pre-empt a problem, prevent oxidation, fine-tune your filtration, avoid unnecessary stabilisation processes and monitor volatile acidity, you will save the money every time. Testing a wine for cold stability might cost £15 or more but if you discover that one wine out of twenty doesn't require cold stabilisation you will have saved the outlay in power alone. Likewise, re-bottling a wine that has proved unstable once bottled will cost you much more than any analysis would have done in the first place.

The parameters tested for the PDO and PGI Wine Schemes are as follows:

Still wines

1. Actual and total alcoholic strengths: a minimum of 8.5 per cent actual alcoholic strength. Total alcoholic strength must not exceed 15 per cent.

2. Reducing sugars: no parameters set: for information only.

3. pH: no parameters set: for information only.

4. Total acidity: a minimum of 4g pr litre expressed as tartaric acid.

5. Volatile acidity: a maximum of: 1.08mg per litre in white and rosé wines

1.2mg per litre in red wine

6. Total sulphur dioxide: the maximum total sulphur dioxide is:

For wines with sugar levels below 5g per litre;

150mg per litre for red wine

200mg per litre for white and rosé wines

For wines with sugar levels above 5g per litre;

200mg per litre for red wines

250mg per litre for white and rosé wines

For wines with sugar levels above 45g per litre;

300mg per litre

7. Free sulphur dioxide: a maximum of 45mg per litre for dry wines as defined in Part B, Annex XIV of Regulation

607/2009; a maximum of 60mg per litre for other wines.

8. Copper: a maximum of 0.5mg per litre.

9. Iron: a maximum of 8mg per litre.

10. Sterility: there must be no indication of yeast or bacteria liable to cause spoilage of the wine.

11. (a) Protein stability: the wine must remain unchanged in appearance after being held at 70°C for 15 minutes and subsequently cooled to 20°C.

11. (b) No-fault tasting: the no-fault tasting (and appeals) can be carried out by the UKVA Wine Scheme Manager: he will ensure that the wine is deemed commercially acceptable.

Sparkling wines

The parameters for PGI an PDO sparkling wines are very similar, with the addition of a pressure test on the bottle, showing at least 3.5 bar pressure plus cold-stability with the wine being clear of tartrate crystals after 36 hours at 2°C. Total SO2 is also set at 185mg/l for sparkling wines.

There are some extra parameters for the top-level PDO scheme, but they are essentially very similar.

Corkwise is the laboratory in the UK that runs these schemes **www.corkwise.net** and all the details for applying can be obtained from the UKVA website or from Corkwise direct.

If you need to check that your wines are within the required parameters before sending off your application for PGI/PDO you can send them into Corkwise separately or to the other laboratory in the UK, Custom Crush UK Ltd **www.customcrush.co.uk**.

You should familiarise yourself with these tests and why they are carried out, as an understanding of that will help with your quality control in the winery.

Storage, riddling and disgorging

If you are making sparkling wine in the traditional, bottle-fermented method you will need plenty of storage for the lees-ageing period. You could have five years' worth of production in storage at any one time. To cut down on space required you can layer the bottles by hand in free-standing stacks. Using stillage cages that are forkliftable are more convenient and will save on time handling the bottles, but they do need more room.

This storage should be within your bonded warehouse area, it should be completely dark with no natural light and preferably low-UV light bulbs, and temperatue-controlled to maintain between 12°C and 16°C.

Your riddling equipment should also be in a dark room where natural light cannot affect the wine – particularly rosés in clear glass bottles. The machines for this process require space, access and three-phase power. The yeast that was introduced at bottling has done its job of creating the bubbles through the second fermentation and providing flavour during the ageing process – autolysis – as the dead yeast cells break down. To remove the yeast and leave a clean, bright wine the riddling process gradually twists and adjusts the bottles until they are completely inverted.

You will also need room for disgorging equipment, corking machines and wire hood applicators. How automated this is will depend on the size of your production. For an average sized UK sparkling winery you will need a semi-automatic line to be able to physically keep up with your production.

After riddling, the bottles are then carefully transferred to have their necks submerged in a freezing glycol bath (at -28°C). Once the plug of yeast is frozen the bottles are rinsed, the crown cap is removed, the frozen plug of yeast is ejected and the bottle is topped up with a sugar and wine solution according to what level of dosage (sugar addition) is required. A cork is inserted and secured with a wire hood. The wine then needs to be returned to storage for some post-disgorging time to allow the dosage liqueur to meld into the wine, before being ready to package and sell.

Oeno Concept in Epernay are the inventors of the Gyropalette, the automated riddling machines. They also supply the cages and disgorging equipment. There are other suppliers of such equipment but you will find most wineries in the UK use the Oeno Concept equipment, which means the level of service is pretty good. **www.oenoconcept.fr**

Packaging and dispatch

Do not underestimate the amount of room you will need for dry goods storage: crown caps, bidules, corks, capsules, foils, glass bottles, cardboard boxes, chemicals, yeasts and additives. All these need to be stored in dry conditions, so the main winery is not suitable. Cardboard packaging should be kept well away from moisture: it can be a source of Trichloroanisole (TCA) in a winery, especially when wet. Consider using plastic pallets rather than wooden ones: these can also harbour TCA bacteria and moulds.

Labelling machines and bottle-washing machines all need space to operate, as well as room for packing into boxes and loading onto pallets. Can the forklift access the area to load the pallets onto trucks? Even if you are small enough scale to be doing this all by hand, you will still need to find space in which to do it.

This area must also be extra secure – packaged wines are a lot easier to steal than single bottles in storage, or indeed wines in tank or barrel. At this stage you have also declared how many bottles you have produced and HMRC will be expecting duty to be paid on each and every bottle as soon as it leaves the bonded area. You need to make sure that your liability for duty is protected (both as a requirement under bonded warehouse regulations and to protect your own revenue).

Think about using six-bottle or twelve-bottle boxes. Twelve bottles of sparkling wine are incredibly heavy and the box itself would have to be fairly substantial. Twelve bottles of still wine weigh approximately 17kg which is fine for one person to lift.

Labelling

The regulations for labelling wine in the UK, and more generally within the EU, are currently in a state of flux, with the recent changes in legislation and their application within the UK still under the process of appeal and definition. Therefore, it would be misleading to print the current status quo as gospel. The best advice is to keep monitoring the UKVA forum and website **www.ukva.org.uk** for the latest updates; there are mock-ups of sample labels on their website but these may change as the current situation develops. The Wine

Standards Board (WSB) is the body within the Food Standards Agency responsible for policing labelling regulations and wine production. Their website carries the old legislation at the moment and may not be updated until the current issues are resolved.

The old Quality Wine Schemes have been replaced with Quality Wine becoming Protected Designation of Origin (PDO), Regional Wine becoming Protected Geographic Indication (PGI) and Varietal Wine as a new category. Table Wine is officially known as wine without geographic indication. The disputes and appeals currently ongoing are regarding the use of 'English' or 'Welsh' wine as a descriptor on the label – as it stands only PDO and PGI wines can use these terms in certain contexts. This comes under the 'Traditional Expression' section detailed below. There are also tighter restrictions on the grape varieties permitted and winemaking practices allowed for the PDO and PGI categories.

The basics that are unlikely to change are taken from the Wine Standards Board guidelines, according to Quality Categories:

For table wine, or wine without a geographic designation

The following compulsory details must be visible on a label without having to turn the bottle:

- Wine/Country of origin
- Bottler's details
- Nominal volume
- Actual alcoholic strength

The following compulsory details are not required in the same field of vision:

- Lot number
- Contains sulphites (or Contains sulphites, sulphur dioxide), in English.

Optional items

Limited optional items are permitted for non-geographic wine e.g. brand name, colour, residual sugar description (e.g. dry, medium dry, see below). Further details are permitted if they do not conflict with specified information and they do not mislead to a material degree. More details below.

Varietal wine category

Only wine approved under a Varietal Wine Certification Scheme can show vine variety(ies) and / or vintage.

For Protected Geographical Indication (PGI) and Protected Designation of Origin (PDO) categories

The following compulsory details must be visible on a label without having to turn the bottle:

- Country of origin.
- A geographical designation .
- A traditional expression
- Protected Geographical Indication/ Protected Designation of Origin.
- Bottler details - name, local administrative address and member state of the responsible bottler; plus exact place where the actual bottling took place if different. Preceded by the words - Bottled by or Bottler.
- Nominal volume.
- Actual alcoholic strength.

The following compulsory details are not required in the same field of vision:

- Lot number.
- Contains sulphites (or Contains sulphites, sulphur dioxide), in English.

PDO and PGI optional items – still wine

Specified optional items permitted include trademarks (brand name), traditional terms, colour, vine variety, vintage. Further details are permitted, providing they do not mislead to a material degree:

- Vine variety – one variety: minimum 85 per cent from the named variety; 2+ varieties: 100 per cent of varieties, in descending order.

- Vintage – wine must be from at least 85 per cent of the named vintage.
- Trademark - trademarks may not be used if they conflict with protected traditional terms or more generally contain misleading information.
- Residual sugar level - for still wines, terms including dry, medium dry, medium, medium sweet, sweet are defined in Regulation 607/2009 – see Annex XIV.
- Traditional terms - "methods of production" Specified terms which have been notified by member states and third countries listed in Annex XII.B of Regulation 607/2009 may only be used by those countries for the category(ies) of wine specified. Examples include "Chateau" (France, Luxembourg), "Reserva" (Spain, Chile).
- Vineyard terms - Specified descriptions may be used only by countries which have notified these to the EC and are listed in Regulation 607/2009 Annex XIII.
- Community symbol - Protected Geographical Indication or Protected Designation of Origin - The symbol authorised by the EC may only be used in addition to the wine category descriptions or Traditional Expression. (For authorised colour versions see Regulation 628/2008).
- Get the PDO/PGI symbols from the UKVA website.

Residual sugar labelling indicators (still wine)

• **Dry**	Maximum of 4g/l, or 9g/l where the total acidity content is not more than 2g/l below the residual sugar content.
• **Medium Dry**	The residual sugar content must exceed the maximum for "Dry" but not exceed 12g/l, or 18g/l where the total acidity content is not more than 10g/l below the sugar content.
• **Medium or Medium Sweet**	The residual sugar content must exceed the maximum for "Medium Dry" but not exceed 45g/l.
• **Sweet**	At least 45g/l.

PDO and PGI – Sparkling wine, compulsory particulars

The following information must appear on a label in one field of vision:

- Wine/Country (provenance)
- Category of product, one of the following defined terms: Sparkling / Quality sparkling wine / Aerated sparkling wine
- Indication of sugar content
- Nominal volume
- Actual alcoholic strength
- The producer or a vendor

The following compulsory details are not required in the same field of vision:

- Contains sulphites (or Contains sulphites, sulphur dioxide), in English.

PDO and PGI optional items – sparkling wine

- Allowed for i) sparkling wine with protected designation of origin or geographical indication; ii) sparkling wine and aerated sparkling wine recognised as varietal:
- Vine variety – one variety: minimum 85 per cent from the named variety;
  2+ varieties: 100 per cent of varieties, in descending order
- Vintage – minimum 85 per cent of stated year.
- Allowed for sparkling wine with protected designation of origin or geographical indication.
- Protected designation of origin/protected geographical indication.

EC wines: one of these terms must be shown together with a geographical indication, unless a traditional term listed by the EC is shown – see eBacchus **http://ec.europa.eu/agriculture/markets/wine/e-bacchus/**

- Community symbol - protected designation of origin/ protected geographical indication.
  The symbol authorised by the EC may only be used in addition to the wine category descriptions.

Case study: Wiston Estate Winery: refurbishing an existing building

Harry and Pip Goring are the current incumbents of Wiston Estate in West Sussex. Harry's family has been in residence for generations farming the land and running the wider estate. It was Pip's dream to plant a vineyard, having grown up surrounded by vines in her native South Africa. They enlisted the help of Dermot Sugrue who, in 2006, was working at Nyetimber Vineyard, also in West Sussex. Dermot left Nyetimber to concentrate on the Wiston project shortly afterwards, planting around 20 acres at Findon to the classic three Champagne varieties of Pinot noir, Pinot meunier and Chardonnay.

Dermot's former life was in financial advice, and one might say that starting a vineyard and winery was not the best financial advice he could have given to the Gorings! But the passion for growing and making wine is never based purely on cold, hard figures, and both Pip Goring and Dermot were smitten with the new project.

By 2008 the vines were starting to mature and the fruit was either going to have to be sold, made under contract elsewhere, or processed on the estate. An old turkey-processing plant on the North Farm site close to Findon was a brave choice as a winery, with Dermot being almost alone in his vision for it as a state-of-the-art facility. The Gorings were persuaded and gave the go-ahead to convert the old building.

The result is not the prettiest visitor-friendly winery, but it does fundamentally work as a winery. Working with an existing building does have its drawbacks. Ceiling heights are fixed, drainage is not easy to retro-fit, power supplies may be restricted. Being a former turkey-processing plant did have some advantages: power was already installed and of decent supply; the drains were in place (most were filled in but could be restored); access for large trucks from the nearby A24 was easy; the heavily insulated rooms for chilled storage are perfect for controlling the second fermentation in bottle, if a little awkward to access.

A feature of the winery is the refurbished Coquard Basket Press, brought over from Champagne. The only one of its kind in the UK, it produces very high-quality juice but is extremely hard work to operate and takes longer than most modern wine presses. The Coquard is situated on the first floor, allowing the juice to be flowed down to the tanks below by gravity. In addition to this basket press the winery also has two modern bladder presses to cope with the influx of fruit at harvest. This extra processing capacity has become vital, as the winery not only processes its own fruit but also makes wine for numerous contract clients from across the UK.

Wiston Estate's first vintage 2008 is very close to being released, and it has recently been announced that Corney & Barrow will be listing the wine.

Wiston Estate, North Farm, Washington, West Sussex, RH20 4BB, Tel 01903 877 745, dermot@wistonestate.co.uk www.wistonestate.co.uk

The current debate for sparkling wines of PDO quality is which grape varieties are allowed to be used. The most recent list is: Pinot noir, Pinot noir precoce, Pinot meunier, Chardonnay, Pinot gris, Pinot blanc. This has caused a few quality sparkling wine producers to feel marginalised for their use of varieties such as Auxerrois. As mentioned before, the whole situation with regards to PDO/PGI regulation is very fluid at the moment, so keep an ear open for new developments.

Winemaking consultants working in the UK

Jean-Manuel Jacquinot

A Champenoise with his own small vineyard and winery in Champagne, Jean-Manuel was the first dedicated sparkling winemaking consultant to work in the UK. Nyetimber Vineyard, when it was first started by Stuart and Sandy Moss in 1986, hired Jean-Manuel to oversee the whole operation. It was only once Nyetimber changed hands for the second time in 2006 that he stopped being so directly involved. At least the third generation of his family to run the Jacquinot Champagne House in Epernay, he has invaluable experience from planting right through to sales and marketing. As well as Nyetimber he has been involved with many more projects in the UK, most recently as the WineSkills Mentor for sparkling wine. This role has seen him visit many new and established wineries offering advice on all aspects of sparkling winemaking.

David Cowderoy

An Englishman with much experience in winemaking across the globe, David and his wife, Jo, are very involved in the UK wine industry (Jo runs the WineSkills programme from Plumpton College) and David is the WineSkills Mentor for still wines. David started his career at Rock Lodge Vineyard in Sussex, moved on to help found Chapel Down, and then spent many years as a flying winemaker across France, Eastern Europe, Italy, Chile, Argentina and Australia.

David and Jo have their own vineyard in the Langeudoc-Roussillon in Southern France, Château La Bouscade.

Owen Elias

Previously the winemaker at Chapel Down for many years, Owen left a few years ago to branch out on his own. Currently working with Hush Heath and Nutbourne Vineyard, amongst others, Owen's consultancy business is called English Terroir. He has been the UKVA's Winemaker of the Year on at least four occasions as well as his wines winning numerous awards at international level. Whilst at Chapel Down, Owen was responsible for making wine for Waitrose, Marks & Spencer, British Airways and Sainsbury's. Over his career he has helped to plant over 150 acres of vineyard land in the UK.

Chapter Five

Marketing

Case Studies

Marketing

English and Welsh wine producers have unique advantages compared to imported wines when it comes to getting their wines to market. The UK has some of the most discerning wine consumers in the world. We also have some of the most active and well-regarded wine writers; London is one of the most important trading centres for wines from all over the world; and it is all on our doorstep. Taking these advantages and making them work for us is not so easy. They can also be seen as a double-edged sword: our wines have to compete with and stand up to the imported wines from classic wine regions and New World vineyards. The UK consumer is used to well-made, fruity, high-alcohol, good-value wines that they can buy for £6 or less. Trying to explain that we, in English and Welsh vineyards, have to contend with low yields, poor weather, erratic harvests, high labour costs, etc. is not good marketing. It is negative, and the consumer might respond with sympathy, but you still haven't given them a positive reason to spend a little more on your wine. Our wines can also be well-made, but we need to accentuate the differences in a positive fashion - subtlety, aromatic rather than fruity, lower in alcohol, and still good value at £10+ for table wines, £25+ for sparkling.

It is not an impossible challenge: the New Zealand wine producers make vastly more wine than their tiny domestic market could possibly consume. They are geographically a long way from anywhere else in the world and rely heavily on exports. We in the UK have a domestic population that could, in theory, drink our production several hundred times over, without shipping further than a couple of hours to London.

New Zealand wines are expensive, in fact, they have the highest average price paid per bottle in the UK even when taking into account the super expensive wines of the classic French regions. This has not stopped them being successful in the UK. The marketing campaign of the New Zealand Winegrowers Association has tied in with the national tourism campaign of New Zealand generally: clean, green – 100% Pure New Zealand. Sustainability and carbon footprinting of wineries has been led by the NZ winegrowers. The consumer is prepared to pay a little bit more for a product they perceive as premium quality (and it helps that the ubiquitous Marlborough Sauvignon blanc is recognisable to even the most uneducated palate).

There is no doubt that New Zealand hasn't got it completely right, and is now suffering slightly from over-production and the potential problems that brings with it, but their strategy as a cohesive group of winegrowers is certainly worth studying.

In the UK we have some organisation of our vineyards in the form of the UK Vineyards Association (UKVA), but it does not get involved with marketing in any form. The English Wine Producers group (EWP) is more relevant to marketing, and it is an organisation that should be the goal of every serious English wine producer to join. Run by its members (who pay substantial sums to take part) and Julia Trustram-Eve, a tireless and indefatigable promoter of the organisation and English wines generally, the EWP is going to become more and more important to the whole industry as we grow and produce more and more commercial volumes of wine.

Any serious entrant to the UK industry should become a member of these organisations as and when they are eligible to do so. DEFRA and the EU, bodies who make and apply the laws governing viticulture in the UK, consult with the UKVA and EWP when legislation is being updated. If you want to have a say in the future of the industry it is worth joining.

While you are in the planning stages it would be worth attending the EWP Annual Tasting held in London, usually in May. You can judge the competition and standard of winemaking you will be up against, plus see the EWP in action. The number of serious wine trade buyers and wine journalists who make the effort to go to this tasting each year is a testament to how successful Julia Trustram-Eve and the EWP have been in putting English wines on the map.

What is your marketing plan?

Marketing is a broad subject and has many applications when talking about the wine production industry. Your strategy will be very much dependent on the size of your production: there is no point approaching the likes of Tesco if you only have 10,000 bottles to sell. With over 2,000 stores in the UK, if you were to sell one bottle of your wine per week in each of their stores you'd need at least 100,000 bottles a year to supply them alone. Now, obviously not every branch carries every line, but this is a crude illustration of the scale on which these supermarkets operate.

Even if you were planning on producing 100,000 bottles per year it would be unwise to totally rely on one client for 100 per cent of your sales. A change of buyer or commercial strategy could see your listing removed at a stroke with no place to go. This chapter is not intended to bash the supermarkets, in fact they can be very valuable outlets as a vineyard's production grows, but care should be taken with the marketing mix to ensure that they are not the sole or majority market for your wine.

A new vineyard will take at least three years to produce a crop, with full production not expected until the vines are over five years old. So, you will have an initially small but increasing supply for which you need to find a market. The early years are a good way to test the market for your wines, whilst you don't have too much stock to sell.

The first few years of your production being small means that the work in the winery will probably not keep you fully employed, and it is tempting to start shouting about what you are doing whilst you have the time. Although it can be argued that all publicity is good, you don't want to risk losing the interest of your market before you have any product to sell them. You want to be turning customers away because you have run out of stock, not because you don't have anything to sell them in the first place: they will go elsewhere and your hard work in raising the profile of English wine will benefit another winery with product to sell.

Decide your strategy now

Whilst you don't want to restrict your potential, it is worth asking yourself what you want to achieve with your vineyard and wine business. Marketing and branding decisions you make now will have far-reaching consequences. Naming your product is probably the

Case study: Breaky Bottom Vineyard, nr Lewes, East Sussex: keeping it local and knowing your market, Peter Hall

Peter Hall planted his first vines in 1974 and has ploughed his own furrow ever since. The stunningly beautiful setting of Breaky Bottom Vineyard, a valley folded deep in the heart of the South Downs, is worth the trip up and down the rutted track. You have to make an appointment before making your trip but you will not be disappointed by either the location or the wines.

Peter's mother was French, and he has a habit of breaking into French when talking about his wines and vinegrowing, but I don't think he'd mind me describing him as eccentrically English. It would be a hard-hearted visitor who was not inspired by his enthusiasm and obvious passion for his wines, and I doubt many leave without their car being weighed down with a few bottles.

Marketing is not something that Peter would imagine he actually does but, whether by default or by design, he has hit the target perfectly. Supply is limited by the size of the property, and what Peter can manage by himself with the help of a dedicated band of friends and family. Harvest each year sees a group of the willing, children included, volunteering to pick the crop in return for some lunch and the experience. It doesn't necessarily make for the most efficient picking, but it is certainly one of the most convivial places to be in October each year. A series of setbacks from pheasants to floods have tried their best to put a stop to the vinegrowing, but Peter does not give in easily and the vineyard bounces back. He supplies Waitrose but, because of his small volumes, the supermarket chain places his wines only in stores within a 30 mile radius of the vineyard. This means the wine generates a feeling of 'localness' with the consumer: it is a low food-miles product because Peter or his wife Christina deliver the wine direct to the stores themselves, cutting out the trucks going to and from a central depot. Sustainability is increasingly important as a marketing tool, and this concentration on the local market enables a loyal following of customers who can then visit the vineyard themselves.

Peter has stuck with Seyval blanc, proving year after year that this variety can produce world-class sparkling wine with a unique English twist. A hybrid grape variety, this is excluded from the top-quality ranking of English wines as it is not a true Vitis vinifera, but Peter has shown repeatedly that with the right care in the vineyard and attention in the winery, Seyval blanc can compete with the best of the Champagne varieties. He does also now produce Chardonnay and Pinot noir, but it is his Seyval that stands out. Mixed with a drop of his homegrown cassis, it produces a uniquely English kir with a fine soft-rose colour and a delicate hint of blackcurrant. By sticking to a narrow range of products that speak of their 'place' and the people involved, Peter is able to sell everything he can make, a lot of it direct from the cellar door.

Contact Peter Hall for an appointment to visit:
Breaky Bottom Vineyard, Rodmell, Lewes, East Sussex, BN7 3EX,
Tel 01273 476 427,
breakybottom@btinternet.com
www.breakybottom.co.uk

most crucial decision – if you brand your wine as 'John's Vineyard', thus tying your product to one specific location, you are restricting your use of that brand to that very particular site. If you never want to expand your production beyond your original site then this is not a problem, and indeed can be a great selling point. But if you have any vision of increasing your production by buying grapes and planting on new sites, then you would have to re-think your branding and product name to cater for that. This is actually enshrined in law. If you put a vineyard name on the label then the wine inside MUST all come from that vineyard.

You might have noticed some of the more dominant names in English wine production have made subtle changes to their brands in recent years. Nyetimber, Ridgeview, Chapel Down and Camel Valley do not make reference to 'vineyard' on any of their labels: all of these wineries source grapes from outside their original 'estate' vineyards so cannot use that term. It doesn't appear to have harmed their appeal, and it is a subtle difference. But be aware of it: re-branding and re-printing labels is expensive and can be avoided by a bit of forethought.

Life is simpler, though not necessarily easier, for the vigneron who limits production and knows they will never want to grow any bigger. They have a goal and can work towards it with total concentration. On the other hand, a larger commercial operation will need to be looking for the opportunities to grow both their supply and subsequent market. Managing demand for the product is essential. Being hard to get hold of, either through limited production and high demand, or selectively releasing stock and selling on an allocation basis, can help create a buzz around a wine. Nothing makes a luxury product (and English wine, particularly sparkling wine, is in the luxury bracket) more appealing than the impression of unavailability. Waiting lists, allocated stock, tiered buying (where the customer has to purchase one case of the lower-end wines to qualify to purchase six bottles of the top release) are all strategies adopted throughout the winemaking world.

In California, top-end Napa Valley wineries have, in the past, very effectively managed their customers and stock to maintain their high prices. Screaming Eagle in Oakville **www.screamingeagle.com** is a case in point; at the moment their website allows you to join the waiting list, with the disclaimer that this does not give you the right to buy their wine, only that you may be moved onto the 'active list' as spaces become available. Several years ago, at the height of the financial boom, even this waiting list was closed to new entrants. In Burgundy, the smaller, in-demand domaines will allocate stock to merchants based on their buying history, allowing each client to buy a limited number of the grands crus in return for them purchasing increasing numbers of the premiers crus and village wines. Domaine de la Romanée Conti is a classic example.

As far as it is possible to tell, so far, these practices have not been either tried or necessary in the UK, but as demand increases for the top sparkling wines, and supply takes its time to catch up, this might become a part of the English wine industry.

Reaching your potential customers – starting small

Your neighbours, friends and family are a good place to start. Get local people involved with the vineyard at planting, by sponsoring a vine, hosting a village party amongst the vines and, later on, at harvest time. It will engage them, get them on your side, and they will become ambassadors for your product wherever they go. It is a small start, but you never know on whose radar you might appear because of it.

This strategy will only take you so far, and you will have to invest more time and money into marketing and branding your product as production grows. Your next stage will be to approach local independent wine merchants and retailers, these guys will have the autonomy to list what they want, and localism is big in retail. Be prepared to give your time and samples to support them in consumer events and tastings at the start and throughout your relationship. The advantage of local retailers is delivery costs are lower – you can do them yourself.

Local restaurants and gastropubs should also be on your radar as the next obvious outlets for your products. English wine is often described as needing to be 'hand-sold', meaning that every bottle has to be recommended by an ambassador. You need to convert the owners

Case study: Camel Valley's Darnibole Vineyard, Cornwall: using competitions and public relations to reach your audience

Bob Lindo, the founder and owner of the hugely successful Camel Valley Vineyard in Cornwall, has scored himself a public relations coup with his 2012 application to the EU and DEFRA for a Protected Designation of Origin (PDO). It is the first independent application for a PDO in England – as the law stands there are only two PDOs in the UK – England and Wales. Camel Valley's request relates to a very small vineyard site (1.5 hectares) within Camel Valley's estate, producing 100 per cent Bacchus grapes, and also applies to how the wine is made. The application not only states that this site is unique, but that the wine it produces is not possible to make anywhere else. It is very restrictive, with the restrictions imposed by the Lindos themselves: the grapes must be hand-picked; no acidification or de-acidification is allowed; neither is chaptalisation (enrichment) permitted; the grapes must reach a higher natural alcohol than legally required in the UK; the wine must be made on-site at Camel Valley; and, finally, the wine must be comparable to previous vintages, ensuring it is typical of the site. The story was covered by the BBC, local and national news, Decanter, The Drinks Business, Harpers and numerous wine blogs and more general food and tourism websites.

Coverage on decanter.com quoted Bob Lindo: Darnibole "tastes different to generic Bacchus. It stands out for its intense, steely minerality and its restrained nose." The Decanter article went on to note that "once it has been approved, Lindo will be able to call his wines 'Darnibole Quality Wine' with no requirement to include 'English' on the label". Cornish devolution in action.

For relatively little time invested, and so far probably not much money, Camel Valley has attracted a huge amount of attention for all the right reasons – the benefits of which will no doubt extend to their entire range of wines. It would not be a surprise if other established vineyards follow suit.

Sam Lindo, Bob's son, is the winemaker for Camel Valley, and has won Winemaker of the Year in the UKVA Annual Awards several times. The

Bacchus wines from the Darnibole site have won numerous gold medals over the years, and the Lindos are relentless at entering (and winning!) competitions both nationally and internationally. They also then use any wins to promote and sell their wines. It is not just the Bacchus which wins awards – the entire range is successful. Sam and Bob's mantras are "make good wine, win something, tell people" and "consistency at every level – no excuses". Quality winemaking is at the heart of their business, as it should be, then letting the wines do their own marketing.

Camel Valley is a prime example of how awards and competitions can be a crucial part of a marketing and publicity campaign if handled correctly. It costs money to enter competitions and also requires investment in terms of time spent, and if you win an award you really need to turn up to accept it to gain maximum exposure. Bear this in mind if you enter competitions abroad. To really capitalise on any wins you must be prepared to follow through.

Camel Valley, Nanstallon, Bodmin, Cornwall, PL30 5LG,
Tel 01208 77659
info@camelvalley.com

of local restaurants, their sommeliers, wine waiters and bar staff to your product. Hold tastings in-house for the staff to find out for themselves how good your wine is. Invite them to the winery for a tour and tasting, visit the vineyard with them and explain the philosophy behind your winemaking. People love a story and a personal connection. Give them a reason to champion your wine and they will do the hard work for you.

Tapping into tourists

If you are on a tourist trail or located in a tourist destination you are lucky, in that other people have done the hard work getting the consumers to your vicinity: now you just need to get them to turn up on your doorstep and buy some wine. Do not under-estimate how much money people will spend when they are on holiday and feel good about life. A consumer who would normally spend £6 per bottle in the supermarket and think they were splashing out, might easily spend double that on a bottle bought from a vineyard after a friendly tour and tasting.

Producers in the West Country have a fresh batch of holidaymakers from all over the UK and abroad each summer, but may struggle in the off-season when the weather puts off all but the most hardy of ramblers. A vineyard situated in the stockbroker belt of Hampshire won't see nearly as many tourists as its neighbours based in the New Forest. When you set up your cellar door sales, think about how much traffic you can reasonably expect, and will it be passing trade? Can you entice people in by leaving leaflets at local B&Bs, pubs and hotels, as well as the tourist office? Be aware of any restrictions placed on you by the local planning and licensing authorities before going too far down this route. You will need to make sure you are legally allowed to receive visitors and sell your wine direct.

It is worth talking to the local tourist office and gauging the potential interest from tourists. Pinpoint the staff and managers/owners from other local tourist spots who might send people on to you. Invite all of them to the winery for a tasting and get them to sell your winery as a tourist destination. This can work particularly well with local pubs who stock your wine.

If you have any other talents or hobbies, such as music or sport, could you host an event or concert that might attract a wider audience to your vineyard? You can then sell your wine to the audience or participants, along with other refreshments. If your vineyard is part of a larger farm you could run a harvest festival (the main arable crops are conveniently harvested before the grape harvest). If you have any livestock, is it possible to offer a 'petting zoo' to attract families? Whilst the children are occupied with lambs or goats, the parents can be tempted with wine tasting and hopefully a purchase to take home.

Farmers' markets

Farmers' Markets are another outlet that can prove useful testing grounds for your wines. They require significant time at weekends and during the week, and you need to be a regular attendant to attract a loyal following. Factor in this time commitment to your business plan. Don't forget to cost your time as well as the direct costs of the stall. Choose your venues carefully, and visit as a customer to see what the competition is in terms of other vineyards. Try to gauge the customer base and the popularity. Be prepared to lose money on the rainy days and average your takings over the season you take a stall.

The great advantage of a market is meeting your customers face to face – if you are offering tasting samples (probably obligatory at these events) then you can get feedback instantaneously. Use this information; make a note of it as it comes in. You can attempt to formalise it by asking customers who taste the wine to make a brief comment on a card, also getting their contact details to add to your customer database. Alternatively, run a business card draw, offering a bottle of wine as the prize, to encourage people to give you their contact details. The Gambling Act 2005 covers prize draws and there are rules for holding prize draws that can be found online at the Gambling Commission website **www.gamblingcommission.gov.uk**, but as long as the draw is open to anyone (over 18, particularly when alcohol is the prize) and free to enter, you will not fall foul of the law. You do not need to apply for permission to hold a free prize draw, and you can charge for entry as long as you abide by these rules:

If you choose to run a free draw with a paid entry route, you must ensure that:

- people can genuinely choose to take part without paying
- the free entry route is no more expensive or no less convenient than the paid route and charged at its normal rate (e.g. the cost of a stamp to send in an entry)
- the choice is publicised so that it is likely to come to the attention of anyone intending to participate
- the system for allocating prizes does not distinguish between either route

Remember that unlike most stallholders at a Farmers' Market, you are selling alcohol, and will need a personal licence to do so (see Chapter Six for more on licensing). This also means that whoever holds that licence will need to be present on the stall, or at least within shouting distance.

Most Farmers' Markets are run by local councils, or on local council property such as the high street of a market town. You will also need to apply to the local council of each venue where you intend to sell for a Temporary Event Notice (TEN). Because most Farmers' Markets are held outside, it is not practical for the organisers to have a premises licence, making the TEN a necessity. It shouldn't be a problem because in most cases the issuing authority will also be the market organiser, however, there is a cost involved in applying for a TEN. Expect to pay £20-£30 for a TEN each time you set up your stall. This is in addition to the stall fee you will be charged. These fees vary from market to market, but expect to pay up to £50 each time and don't forget to check whether you get a stand, canopy, table, etc. included with your fee.

Finding your local Farmers' Markets is fairly straightforward. If the organisers of your nearest market are doing a half-decent job then you should have seen advertising in your local area. Try the local councils in a 30-mile radius of your vineyard, or a simple Google search will throw up some starting points. Also look at the National Farmers' Retail & Market Association (FARMA); **www.farma.org.uk**, and specifically the markets section at **www.localfoods.org.uk**.

Cellar door sales

You need to decide whether you want to sell your wines from the cellar door, and to what extent. Will you have a dedicated tasting room and shop, charge for tours and employ the hard-sell to each and every visitor, or will it be more ad hoc and by appointment only for bespoke tours? This decision will be influenced by your location – if you are on a tourist trail with lots of passing trade then you may find that having set opening hours and a dedicated member of staff to undertake tours and sell the wine will be worth the investment. Be aware that you will need a licence to sell alcohol off the premises. The local council's planning office will also take an interest: if you are selling only your own products, grown and made on site, then you will likely have no problems doing tours and tastings by appointment, however, opening a shop with potential to sell other local produce and encouraging drop-in visitors will mean that the access must be suitable and won't cause a hazard, the increase in traffic should not impact on your neighbours, the business signage should be appropriate to the area, and adequate parking must be available.

Do not view the planning officers as the enemy – their job is not to prevent you doing business but to make sure that your business does not have a detrimental effect on those people living around you. Work with them and be prepared to do some homework yourself. Vineyards are not yet that common, and most planning officers will not have had to deal with one. There is some confusion within planning departments across the country as to exactly what category a vineyard and winery falls into. This is discussed in more detail in the winemaking chapter, but for your marketing plan the council will be interested if a retail outlet is planned, visitors are expected, traffic increases, and what signage is erected. Very simply, if you plan on selling only your own products, grown on your vineyard, then the justification is easier to make. It becomes a grey area when contract winemaking is taking place, thus moving from pure agricultural use to light industrial, or if products other than your own are being sold from the premises.

There is a case that went before the Secretary of State – David Millington, of Wroxeter Roman Vineyard in Shropshire, was served

Case study: Bolney Wine Estate: re-branding

This is a good example of a vineyard that has ridden out the highs and lows of the English wine industry over the last few decades by not being afraid to adapt. Bolney Wine Estate, formerly Booker's Vineyard, was established in 1972 and has been owned by the same family ever since. During the lifetime of the company, the wines and their packaging have evolved to meet current trends, with the latest major overhaul in 2010/2011. The previous designs were looking dated and were not cohesive across the range. Sam Linter, the winemaker and daughter of the founder, made the decision that the labels needed to express a higher quality image, reflecting both the improved quality of the wines and the innovation of the winery as a whole.

Barlow Doherty, the specialist wine label design team, was commissioned to take the design of the label along with the corporate identity to the next level. The results were very well received, featuring the family nature of the estate, with the resident dogs taking centre stage. The labels, as well as the wines, won awards at the UKVA Annual Competition, and it was widely regarded as a successful re-branding. Since that change, the wines themselves have continued to improve in quality and achieve even greater recognition on the international and domestic competition circuit. A natural evolution for Bolney Wine Estate was to upgrade the labels further, keeping the intrinsic nature of Barlow Doherty's original design, which works very well, and moving the overall corporate image towards one of top-end quality English wines. Whilst featuring the dogs on the label is very friendly and non-threatening to the consumer, there is a risk that the artisanal appeal will put off the higher-end customers, such as fine dining restaurants, etc. Therefore, the winery is undergoing a refinement of the new label design to attract a wider audience. The changes will be subtle but crucial in taking the brand to a wider market.

The range of wines at Bolney is extensive, and includes entry-level still white, rosé and red under the Lychgate label, up to a single vineyard Pinot noir that sells out within weeks of going on sale. There is also an extensive range of sparkling wines, including a sparkling red wine: this is possibly unique within the UK, sparkling red wine is more often associated with Australian Shiraz. It is the perfect accompaniment to a barbecue.

Sam Linter is a pioneer of English red wines and has rightly won accolades for her barrel-fermented blends and single varietal Pinot noirs. Red wine is a hard sell for most English wineries; the style is usually light and fruity but has a price tag way above juicy, ripe New World wines. Sam's vineyard selection, investment in quality equipment such as sorting tables, experimentation with different yeasts and judicious use of oak, means her reds stand out from the crowd and Bolney consistently produces red wines that can compete on the international stage. The vineyard is open to visitors year round, and tours and tastings can be booked in advance.

Bolney Wine Estate at Bookers Vineyard, Foxhole Lane, Bolney, West Sussex RH17 5NB,

Tel 01444 881 575

www.bolneywine.co.uk

with an Enforcement Notice by the local planning authority after neigbours complained of increased traffic, both cars and coaches, visiting the vineyard site. The Notice claimed that tours, tasting and selling of wine was not agricultural use, despite the wines being sold only coming from the farm vineyards, therefore Mr Millington must desist from these commercial activities. Although the outcome of the appeals and subsequent rulings are far from clear, they have been used since to back up planning applications for commercial activity by vineyards. The full transcript of the case can be found at **www.bailii.org/ew/cases/EWCA/Civ/1999/1682.html**.

Matthew Bernstein, the owner of Kenton Vineyard in Devon and a former lawyer, summed up his experiences with the local planning authority, using the transcript of the case, and contributed the following to the UK Vineyard Association email forum as follows:

"It's fairly abstruse stuff, which to a large extent turns on certain technical points, but my understanding is that it has established that a winery which is used to make wine from grapes grown on that holding constitutes agricultural use, This position was accepted by our Local Authority when we built our winery: no change of use was required to turn an existing agricultural building into a winery. The position is probably different if the winery is to make wine for others."

Matthew goes on to point out one of the Judge's summing up was quite clear with his recommendations, as the case was referred back to the Secretary of State:

"For generations, in Somerset and elsewhere they have been making cider on the farm. To suggest that it is not a farming activity or ancillary to the growing of apples would be an affront to common sense. The Secretary of State accepts that wine making should not receive any different treatment. No doubt he will bear that in mind." Lord Justice Mantell

Taking your wine from local to national level

You do not want to attempt any serious national launch until you have enough stock to sell, although some 'soft' marketing will not harm your reputation. By this I mean you should encourage any trade and press contacts you have to visit and taste. An initial press release could be sent out once your plans are finalised, and again when anything is happening in the winery or vineyard that warrants a photo opportunity: tanks being delivered, pickers working in the vineyard, the first disgorging or bottling – anything that makes a good photograph and has a bit of a story to go with it. If you can't get key people from the press or trade to come to the site then keep letting them know what is going on at crucial stages – to keep their attention/interest.

It is important to not only focus on the big-name consumer journalists but also target the writers for the trade magazines such as Harpers, The Drinks Business, etc. If the trade become aware of a new winery as it gets established they might be more prepared to consider stocking the wine once it is available.

Don't forget the local press – they may not be wine specialists, but sometimes the national newspapers will pick up a news item from the regional news and disseminate it further (see case study on Camel Valley). Vineyards and wineries can be picturesque, offering a good filming or photographic opportunity for local television, web and print media.

Competitions

Once your wine is available in bottles, for sale, it is important to enter some competitions to gain recognition. You can start with the Regional Vineyard Associations, most of which will hold a small competition. The UKVA Wines of the Year Competition is the next step outside your local area. The wine will be up against the best from the UK (and the worst!) and, if it is possible to establish the wine's quality within the sector, compared to its peers, then that can be used as a launch pad from which to jump into the international competition scene. The International Wine and Spirit Competition (IWSC) has a category for best sparkling wine in the world (outside Champagne). Nyetimber has won it at least twice. Ridgeview has won Gold medals at the Decanter World Wine Awards 2010. Chapel Down and Denbies Wine Estate both scooped Golds at the International Wine Challenge 2011. These competition wins have put English wine firmly on the map, particularly for sparkling wines.

If you are going to compete with these guys at this level, you will need to make sure you are ready. Patience is required: early harvests tend not to be of a fantastic quality, so only release a wine with decent lees-age in the case of sparkling, and from a good vintage, to stand a chance. You don't want to do badly and risk alienating the wine trade at an early stage.

The competitions you enter should be chosen with recognition, image and validity in mind: which award? who is judging it? And which are the other wines, if any, it would be up against?

The following paragraph is from the English Wine Producers website, reporting on the awards announced at the 2009 London International Wine Fair: "the Decanter World Wine Awards introduced a UK category for the first time this year and were rewarded with an impressive number of entries, of which 86% gained an award, including two gold medals. As only 2.8% of the entries in the whole competition won a gold medal, this single success from England has shown the quality of the category. The two gold medals were awarded to sparkling wines: Camel Valley White Pinot 2005 and Hush Heath's Balfour Brut Rosé 2005. The latter took the trophy for best English wine, and qualified for the competition's Trophy Tasting."

Whilst not wanting to belittle their achievements, note the figure in the first sentence – 86 per cent of entries gained an award. Eighty six percent! Either it means the overall standard of English wine entered was very high or, if one were being cynical, the judges were very sympathetic. The figure of only 2.8 per cent of total entries gaining a gold is more impressive for the two wines involved, and all credit to them, however, the Camel Valley wine was not available for sale about a millisecond after the results were announced and was always limited. The Balfour Brut is very expensive (one of the most expensive English wines available) and again, in limited quantities. There is no doubt that these successes will have a knock-on effect for the other wines made by those wineries, but be wary of having to disappoint customers.

Apart from the UKVA's own award ceremony, there is one other tasting competition's results that have been eagerly anticipated by the industry each of the two years it has been run. The Judgement of Parson's Green, run by Stephen Skelton MW, featured 94 wines in the 2012 line-up, four of which were 'ringers', ie. not English wine but Champagne or high-end New World sparkling wines. Only one of these ringers made it into the top 30, Sainsbury's Blanc de blancs Champagne (made by Duval Leroy). The tasting was attended by a panel of Masters of Wine including the doyenne of wine critics Jancis Robinson. Her presence and subsequent coverage on her website, **www.jancisrobinson.com**, spurred wider coverage by the wine press.

The wines that made the top of the list were a mixed bag representing all styles of English sparkling wine from rosé to blanc de blancs, some with long lees-ageing, others released with only the minimum nine months on lees. The dominating factor of the top wines was that they were all made with the classic three champagne varieties – with the honourable exception of Breaky Bottom's 2006 Seyval blanc. Another factor that linked the best-performing wines was a relatively high dosage level of around 10g/l. This flies in the face of the current trend for zero- or low-dosage Champagnes. English wines tend to have a higher acidity than their continental counterparts, which may explain the preference for a higher balancing sugar content.

Websites and online presence

Being online no longer only means having a website: social networking is a feature of many businesses. Facebook and Twitter are two obvious portals that offer a cheap and easy way to reach many potential customers and their friends. You still need a website for the customer to go to after being alerted to your existence by their social network of choice. The crucial thing to remember when embarking on a social networking presence is to be current and up to date. It doesn't mean tweeting six times a day or updating your Facebook page/blog every day, but it does mean that you need to have fresh content on a regular basis. People will lose interest if they see the same piece of news every time they log on. The benefit of Twitter is that it doesn't have to be ground-breaking news each time, in 140 characters you can let people know that you are pruning in the snow/sun/rain, that you are bottling your first vintage, prepping the winery for harvest, taking delivery of new tanks, designing a new label – anything and everything that you do towards getting your wine to the market can be tweeted.

Case study: Kenton Vineyard, Devon: Matthew and Jo Bernstein

Matthew and Jo Bernstein left their respective careers in law and medicine behind them when they set up Kenton Vineyard at Helwell Barton in Devon. Prior to taking the plunge, Matthew enrolled at Plumpton College to gain the book learning and practical skills necessary for establishing and running a vineyard. Only then did the exhaustive search begin for the perfect vineyard plot that would also enable them to live on-site. Helwell Barton, a tiny hamlet close to Kenton in Devon, offered the perfect combination of a dilapidated farmhouse adjacent to a free-draining, south-facing slope ideal for vines. Several years later Matthew is turning out thousands of bottles of red, white and rosé on an annual basis, along with a wonderful sparkling wine made from Ortega and Auxerrois. Each vintage reinforces the choice they made as the right one. The rigour and attention to detail that Matthew applied to his previous career as an intellectual property lawyer has been apparently seamlessly transferred to his vine-growing and winemaking endeavours.

The vineyard employs a high-maintenance but very high-quality double canopy trellising system known as Scott Henry, and the results speak for themselves: the ripeness levels Matthew achieves in his red wines surpass anything the author has seen in other vineyards across the UK. .

The winery building has a tasting room, initially open to the public on a daily basis. However, the Bernsteins soon discovered that this can be a millstone around the neck of a small producer. Not big or busy enough to justify dedicated staff to run, the onus was on Matthew and Jo to be there all the time and be available to respond when visitors rocked up on a whim. So Matthew and Jo made the decision to close the tasting room for ad-hoc visits and sales.

They now offer tours and tastings to pre-booked groups – this ensures that the visitors who do come are serious about English wine and are more likely to buy if they like the wines.

www.kentonvineyard.co.uk

It requires a certain dedication, but needn't be time consuming.

Your website should be informative, and can tell the visitor more about the story of you and your vineyard, with lots of photographs and snippets of information, along with an online shop when you have stock to sell. You can use it to advertise tastings, events and new releases, and drive people to it via your social networking activity. The cost of running a website need not be expensive, though it does have a cost implication. The cost of design can range from a few hundred pounds to thousands, depending on the functionality of it. A webshop will be more expensive to set up and maintain than a simple, informative site. The hosting of a website can also be very inexpensive: the cost of hosting a website and domain name can be as low as £10 per year.

Visit as many other vineyard websites as you can, particularly those who are offering a similar product to you. When selecting a web designer make a note of your favourite winery websites and ensure that the person you select has a sympathetic style – you should be able to see other websites they have designed to make sure they will understand your style and ethos.

Whilst having an online shop may seem tempting, and a cheap way to reach customers, you need to have the ability to ship your wine to your clients. This may not seem like a problem, but finding couriers who will take liquids is one thing, then finding one who will take liquid in a glass bottle is another. Should you surmount these problems and find a courier who will take your wine for shipping, you have to contend with the inevitable breakages, thefts and losses along the way. If one bottle breaks in a case it often means that the others become unsaleable as the labels are damaged. You then need to get that case back and re-dispatch to the customer. With a good courier this shouldn't happen too often, but it will happen occasionally so you need to have a plan to cope with it and be making enough margin to absorb the costs. Not forgetting that one of these costs will be extra packaging to give your wine the best chance of making it to the customer in once piece. At least with wine being a fairly high-value product, it is easier to absorb this cost, but margins are usually slim at the best of times, so don't forget to factor it in.

When selling online and sending your product direct to the consumer, you will need a premises licence. It should be a formality because there is no impact on the locality in terms of visitors and drinking on-site, but again it is a consideration that shouldn't be forgotten.

If you don't want to maintain a shop online, then your site can instead drive customers to your distributors and retailers. It is best to work out your technological limitations and work with them. If you are not naturally inclined towards a high-maintenance online presence, then use your site simply to provide information about your wines. If you don't already make use of Twitter, Facebook, LinkedIn and use e-commerce yourself, then you are unlikely to make a success of these options without feeling it is a lot of hard work. Having said that, if you have anyone working with you or a member of the family to whom an online life is second nature, then get them to do it for you.

Don't overlook the chance to collect data on your customers and website visitors whilst they are browsing. Offer them the chance to follow you on Twitter, link them to your Facebook page where they can 'friend' you, and gather contact information via an email newsletter. Make sure you then do actually send a regular newsletter offering the chance to buy early-release wines, inform people of progress in the vineyard and winery, invite them to events, etc. Be aware that collecting data from people means you must comply with the Data Protection Act 1998, essentially to ensure that you don't share anyone's data with others without their permission, and don't use it for any reason other than that stated when it was collected. The most common error is sending a group email to your entire list without using the BCC (blind copy) function.

Labels and packaging

Once your wine is out of your hands and sitting on the shelf of a shop, it needs to speak for itself at first glance. Unless there is a tasting going on, or the staff have decided/been persuaded to hand-sell your wine, then your label needs to do everything you would normally do to sell your wine and more. Remember, it will be sat on the shelf next to an endless array of other wines.

Still wines and sparkling wines have very different expectations held of them in terms of packaging. A still wine can afford to be a bit

different, and have a quirky or trendy design. Something along those lines can often help sales on looks alone. Think of the arty or graphic images on some of the first Australian and other New World wines that made it to the UK in the 1980s and 1990s. Sparkling wine, however, is a different story. The customer expects something a bit special when they spend the extra money on a Champagne or top-end sparkling wine. If you look at the range of English sparkling wines on the shelf they are all traditional in style and are often similar to Champagne labels with the use of serif fonts and gold or silver embossing.

If you have a range of wines, you will need to allow for the differences to be reflected in the labels, whilst maintaining a consistent identity. This can be especially difficult if you have both still and sparkling wines. A good label designer should be able to work around the problem, given a comprehensive brief. You will need to have an idea in mind about what level you are pitching at, and what image you want your labels to portray: a designer can only work with the information you give them. If you request a rustic feel that reflects your farming roots, you can't then complain that the label is not upmarket enough!

There are obviously also legal requirements for labelling (*see* Chapter 5) but remember that your 'front' label, containing all the boring legal information, can to all intents and purposes be your back label. The retailer will make the decision as to which way round to face the bottle – if the clean lines and modern design of your back label are more attractive than the legal front label, there is no law that states the front label has to be faced to the front on the shelf. The customer also expects to turn the bottle around and read about the wine. This is your chance to tell them what you think of your wine, write your own tasting note, tell them what food to eat with the wine, and let them know where they can get more information via your website. Use a QR code to drive traffic to your website – a 'Quick Response' code (see picture below) allows the owner of a smartphone with a barcode reader app to scan the label and be taken to your webpage. This is your opportunity to persuade them to go ahead and buy the wine, tell them where they can buy it (if they have come across it at a friend's house), visit your winery, tweet to their followers that they just drank this wonderful wine, etc. The opportunities are endless.

Chapter Six

Other income opportunities

Case Studies

Other income opportunities

Wine tourism is extremely popular in many wine regions in numerous countries worldwide, especially New Zealand, California, Rioja, Australia, South Africa and Germany. Onsite activities raise the profile of the winery and brand, increase income, and can create employment opportunities. In the UK, Denbies Wine Estate, Surrey **www.denbiesvineyard.co.uk** offers facilities for use by the general public, including conference and wedding facilities, a restaurant, art exhibition space, and even a vineyard train. Not all UK vineyards and wineries are open to the public, as many prefer to concentrate on the quality of their wine and winemaking facilities. Furthermore, initial costs associated with building and setting up a visitors centre or cellar door facility can be constrained by finances. However, many activities that bring people to the vineyard do not need an initial cash injection and can engage people with the vineyard and winery. Vineyard tours and wine tastings are a good starting point, and can be part of English Wine Week **www.englishwineweek.co.uk**, organised by the English Wine Producers **www.englishwineproducers.com**, in the first week of June every year. If you want to use outside wine educators, then the Association of Wine Educators (AWE) **www.wineeducators.co.uk** has a full list of members available for delivering wine courses and tastings. Prior to deciding on visitor hospitality for your business, visit a range of vineyards and wineries in the UK, taste their wines, and experience what is currently on offer to visitors. This chapter makes suggestions for other sources of income for UK vineyards and wineries in order to increase wine sales and income, and to raise brand awareness, both locally and nationally.

Vineyard and winery tours

Many small, medium and large vineyards conduct tours of their facilities that are carried out by existing staff or specially employed part time seasonal staff. Court Garden Vineyard, Sussex **www.courtgarden.com** offers small group vineyard tours with the owner, Howard Corney, at 3pm on Saturday afternoons. The cost is £8 and the group meets in the beautiful Sussex Barn where they are served tea and homemade cake, before listening to a short talk about the history of vine growing in England. They go on a short walk around the vineyard and discuss the vineyard work carried out throughout the year. The tour includes a tasting of their sparkling wines, made by Hattingley Valley Winery, Hampshire, and well-known Champagne. Additionally gift vouchers for tours can be sold as presents which the recipient can use at a future date and guarantees income to the vineyard. Vineyard tours can be advertised via websites with online booking facilities or by telephone to ensure advance bookings. The Office of Fair Trade (OFT) has launched a useful online resource to help businesses comply with the law when selling goods and services at a distance. The Distance Selling Hub is available at **www.oft.gov.uk/distanceselling** and provides information about the rules and regulations that apply to the sale of goods and services over the internet, telephone, by text or by mail order.

It is important to make sure that there are parking facilities for cars and / or coaches for large groups if you decide to offer them. Standard tours of vineyards and wineries in the UK range from £3 to £12, depending on the vineyard, content of the tour, tour length, and whether they are led by a guide. The award-winning and internationally renowned Ridgeview Estate in Sussex, **www.ridgeview.co.uk** offers tours, Chapel Down in Kent **www.chapeldown.com** offers standard tours and more expensive gift experience packages, which include a meal in their restaurant. Eglantine Vineyard, Nottinghamshire **www.eglantinevineyard.co.uk** has open days three times a year, in addition to two hour group tours for ten or more people costing £5 per person. Holmfirth Vineyard, Yorkshire **www.holmfirthvineyard.com** offers vineyard tours for 1 ½ - 2 hours, costing £5.50, plus Sparkling Afternoon Tea for Two costing £29.99. Nutbourne Vineyard, West Sussex **www.nutbournevineyards.com** offers tours of the vineyard, lake, llamas and the beautiful converted mill which, for £30 per person, can include a barbecue and tutored tasting. Tours of your premises and facilities provide visitors with a memorable experience which can also culminate in wine sales and recommendations to family and friends. They can be organised for set times each week, or by appointment with the winery via the website or telephone, with costs and tour contents agreed in consultation with staff.

Considering the widespread use of social media and mobile technology, their use by UK vineyards to publicise tours and activities is still limited: tour details are tweeted on Twitter by only a few wineries. Unlike vineyards and wineries around the world, there is also limited use of Facebook pages, groups or events to promote tours or activities in the UK. Likewise there is limited use of vineyard or winery videos on YouTube, or the use of smart phone applications, or a presence on LinkedIn and other social media sites. These are free, cheap tools that rapidly reach many people, and an active social network presence can increase vineyard, winery and brand awareness thereby increasing visitors to your business and therefore your income. Regular updates, photographs, events and vineyard news can be posted on social network sites or tweeted.

Local tourism initiatives

New vineyards could join with other local vineyards to promote a combined vineyard trail and tours, in conjunction with the local tourist board. Some vineyards already do this independently as with Tourism South East **www.visitsoutheastengland.com** and Visit the Heart of England **www.visitheartofengland.com**. Tourism initiatives, such as local food and drink campaigns as part of destination marketing, result in an increased awareness of your vineyard and winery, via promotions on local tourism sites and participation in their local attraction marketing campaigns. Some small UK vineyard owners often have full time day time employment, and any spare time is spent working in the vineyard, resulting in limited time to conduct or organise tours. However, tourist destinations like Jersey, the Isle of Wight, Wales and the Isles of Scilly, all have vineyards and a ready-made tourist market to sell their wines to. The vineyard on the Isles of Scilly is situated on St. Martin's, the third largest of the five inhabited islands **www.stmartinsvineyard.co.uk**. Sark has an organic vineyard owned by Sir David and Sir Frederick Barclay, and Sark Vineyards released its first wine in 2011 under the direction of Bordeaux winemaker Dr Alain Raynaud. The new wine is an experimental blend of Savagnin, Chardonnay and Pinot gris from the first 30,000 of the 100,000 vines planted on Sark. Chef Peter Gottgens, owner of the Ardeonaig Hotel in Perthshire, Scotland, planted his own vineyard which is the only vineyard in Scotland!

Country houses

There are several historical and beautiful country houses in the UK that have vineyards planted in the grounds, for example Stanlake Park, Twyford, Berkshire **www.stanlakepark.com**. The original test vineyard of 500 vines, planted in 1979, was called Thames Valley Vineyard (later changed to Valley Vineyards). This is now 25 acres planted with over 20,000 vines. There are different trellising systems used, including some unique to the estate – the 'Stanlake Bow' and the 'Stanlake Ballerina', which is a variant of the Smart-Dyson Ballerina, a mid-height Sylvoz system. Winemaking takes place in the 17th-century Reformation barn, and the marketing led approach is focused on developing the Stanlake Park brand name. The 800 year-old Squerryes Court, Westerham, Kent **www.squerryes.co.uk** has a vineyard, and Broadfield Court, Bodenham, Herefordshire **www.broadfieldcourt.co.uk** is a medieval manor house that planted fifty experimental vines in 1971 and now covers 17 acres. Ickworth House, Suffolk **www.ickworthvineyard.co.uk** has a five acre vineyard that surrounds the 1st Earl of Bristol's summerhouse, built in 1703. There are others such as Leeds Castle, Kent, Renishaw Hall, North Derbyshire and Wiston Estate, West Sussex. Pinot noir, Chardonnay and Pinot meunier varieties have been planted in 3 hectares (7.4 acres) of Windsor Great Park, owned by the Crown Estate, with the involvement of Laithwaites Wines. Whether more stately homes and country houses will plant vines is unknown at present, but with a ready-made visitor market for their wines more may appear in the future. Their wine could be made at a contract winery to limit initial outlay, but vineyard set-up costs and maintenance requirements still need to be considered.

Visitors centres

You do not have to have a special tasting room for visitors on tours, as a couple of oak barrels to put the wine glasses on in the winery can be exciting and appealing to visitors. If you are keen to have a visitor centre or cellar door with a tasting room, then you will need to seek planning permission and building regulations approval from your local authority. It is more complicated for listed buildings and conservation areas, but is slightly easier if you wish to convert an existing agricultural building. This can be a lengthy process, so it is best to start with the government website and follow the link **www.direct.gov.uk/en/HomeAndCommunity/Planning/PlanningPermission/DG_4018203**. Your business plan should include these plans and contain staffing costs, parking facilities, disabled access, hours of business, events, activities, income projections and initial financial outlay. Setting up credit card payment, staff payments and tax, business rate charges, VAT, staff training and building maintenance as well as any potential future business expansion, all need to be included in the plans. Furleigh Estate, Dorset **www.furleighestate.co.uk** opened a new cellar door and tasting room in April 2012, and the building and conversion of the existing property took six months to complete. The cellar door will be open from every Friday and Saturday 11am – 4pm, for tours and tastings. Other wineries which have visitor centres/ cellar door facilities with wine shops include Chapel Down, Kent **www.chapeldown.com**, Sharpham Estate, Devon **www.sharpham.com** and Three Choirs, Gloucestershire **www.three-choirs-vineyards.co.uk**. Halfpenny Green Vineyard, South Staffordshire **www.halfpenny-green-vineyards.co.uk** offers a range of activities from tea rooms, crafts and tours to fishing. Cellar doors and onsite shops do not just give you a place to sell direct to the customer, they can also offer food, accommodation and wine-related activities and products. Your employees are the ambassadors of your brand, so they need training in your product. Additionally, in line with your marketing strategy (*see* Chapter 5), branding should continue throughout the facilities with attention to buildings, signage and grounds. Family-focused activities and links with countryside events, like nature trails that schools can benefit from, are worth considering, allowing engagement with the local community.

Case study: Bolney Wine Estate, East Sussex:

One of Bolney Wine Estate's main ventures is their vineyard tours and tastings. It is a valuable source of income and they believe it is vitally important in educating the general public on the subject of English wine. With the greater interest in local produce, especially for locally sourced English wine, it is a fantastic time to be producing wine in England. The tours are extremely popular, and the customers really enjoy the wine that they taste.

When running tours and tastings there are lots of things to consider, one of the most important of which is health and safety procedures and risk assessments. The staff at Bolney take ten minutes before each tour to talk the group through health and safety in the vineyard and fire procedures. Every tour script and outline is consistent, although each Bolney Wine Estate tour guide has their own personal style! Great care must be taken when writing copies for the website and vouchers. Customers come to the estate with certain expectations, and it is important to make sure that the experience matches them. You also have to be ready for criticism, and accept that not everyone is going to enjoy your wine no matter how good it is! The Bolney Estate tours include a walk around the vines, and a visit to the winery, where customers learn about winemaking, the vines, English wine and the history of the estate. The tours end with a tutored tasting and quite often a lunch or cream tea! The tour guide stays with them throughout the whole tour for a more personal touch. The estate caters for the tours themselves, and a lot of thought goes into this because they try to source all of the food locally, i.e. cheese from the High Weald Dairy in West Sussex. Eating local produce is a very popular notion these days, and to be successful in your business you have to have a good relationship with your local partners and work together to promote the produce from your local area. Bolney Wine Estate feels that it is important to have good relationships with other vineyards in the UK as each of them is promoting English wine.

In order to advertise the tours, Bolney Wine Estate sell their vouchers through gift companies, as well as through their ow website.

The plan for the future is to have a Vineyard Café and eventually a proper visitors centre. Customers expect a lot from the facilities and in September (the busiest tourism month) they have a high demand for space and are stretched to their limit. They would love customers to be able to visit them on a more flexible basis because more and more people like to drop into the shop in the interest of lowering food miles.

When planning a venture such as opening a café you need to get the ball rolling as soon as possible, as it can take months to get planning permission. In Bolney's case they were told to forget having the visitors centre at the top of their field, where they wanted it, as they would never get the planning permission due to residents nearby. As for their café project, which is a simple extension onto an existing building, it has required much planning and, even though it is their own land, they still need permission. Even planning a road sign takes time: when they made an enquiry to the local council about a road sign, they were told it could take up to ten days just to respond to their initial enquiry!

There are a wide range of things you can sell in a vineyard shop aside from the wine you produce. At Bolney Wine Estate they sell their own jams and chutneys along with the wine in the shop. They cannot sell any items which are not made at Bolney Wine Estate, as they would need to pay different business rates to sell other products, but as they are in the process of changing their business rates to run their café, in the future they will be able to sell products from other local producers. It is not easy to sell produce other than wine without a proper shop onsite, unless every product you sell has a relevance to wine or the vineyard business. Most of Bolney's wine is sold through the tours, and the guests taste the chutney and jam in different meal options, leading to a rise in their sales of secondary products. You also need a licence to sell the wine. The owner, and all tour guides and staff selling the product, have to go on personal licence courses if you want them to sell wine at shows and events etc. It is worth it, as these can be an excellent way for people to find out about your wine.

www.bolneywineestate.co.uk

Café, tea rooms and restaurant

If you are considering an onsite café, tea room or restaurant then the first thing you will need is planning permission, either to change the existing building to a licensed premises or to construct a specific building. Applying for a licence means that regulations need to be adhered to and magistrates will visit to check the proposal and fire regulations. There are several organisations to approach for help and guidance, and a good starting point is "Run a Restaurant" **www.runarestaurant.co.uk**, which offers advice about setting up a restaurant, building and planning regulations, insurance, staff, catering, health and safety, and business rates. Small business information, including legal advice, government grants, and business funding and insurance can also be sought from **www.smallbusiness.co.uk**. Business Link is able to provide support for training and funding **www.businesslink.gov.uk**. You will have an assessment to enable them to find out about your business; they may send an advisor to your home or business premises. They also advise on match funding for IT related aspects like setting up a website and help with marketing issues, graphic designers and printers. Business Link also has information for farmers regarding the special VAT scheme known as the flat rate scheme. It is for farmers that are not registered for VAT and consequently cannot reclaim tax. However, they can charge and keep a flat rate addition of 4 per cent when they sell qualifying goods or services to VAT-registered customers. This is not VAT, but acts as compensation for losing tax on purchases. The flat rate addition is part of the business takings and should be included in sales.

If you decide to open a restaurant on the vineyard premises it is important to know your local restaurants and coffee shops, in order to understand the market for the local community and type of visitors to the region. This should be a major part of your business plan and, to attract funding, you need to know your potential local business competitors, those that succeed and those that failed. Accommodation in the area is also relevant for potential customers to the restaurant. This information will contribute to decisions such as your menu, hours of business, size of the restaurant, type of staff required, food suppliers and branding. Vineyards and wineries with a restaurant on the premises can also offer cookery courses and food and wine matching courses, and cater for special events such as birthdays and corporate dinners. Many UK vineyards offer food and drink premises, including Highdown Vineyard, West Sussex **www.highdown-vineyard.co.uk**, which has a tea room in a converted barn. Jabajak Vineyard, Carmarthenshire, Wales, offers an à la carte menu in its four bistros **www.jabajak.co.uk**, and Wyken Vineyard, Bury St Edmonds, Suffolk, has a vineyard restaurant in a beautiful 400-year-old barn **www.wykenvineyards.co.uk**. Hattingley Valley vineyard, Hampshire **www.hattingleyvalley.co.uk**, organises a range of diverse events and entertainment options for corporate functions. Their tasting room can provide a venue for an informal reception, conference or sit-down meal for up to 24 guests. Amber Valley Wines, Derbyshire **www.ambervalleywines.co.uk**, which started planting in 2011, with further plantings in 2012, is planning a micro-winery, a café/restaurant and delicatessen, for local produce to be served and sold together with their own, and local wines. They will use contract grape growers in the area to supplement their fruit, who will need to commit to a minimum of 15 years. Camel Valley, Bodmin, Cornwall **www.camelvalley.com** showed in 2011 that you can make high-quality wine in the UK and still make the most of other income streams, by hosting a fish barbecue prepared by double Michelin-starred chef Nathan Outlaw.

Alcohol licensing

A Personal Licence for the sale of alcohol (England and Wales) is required for all staff selling alcohol on licensed premises, to ensure that every sale is authorised by a personal licence holder. The Licensing Act 2003 established the granting of personal licences to individuals to supply, or to authorise the supply of alcohol. The Personal Licence is separate from the licence that authorises properties to be used for the supply of alcohol. The licensing of individuals and unconnected to the licensing of premises, allows personal licence holders to move from one place to another. Applicants must be 18 years or older and must apply to their local authority. Once granted it is valid for ten years.

Case study: Southern Slope Vineyard, Panniers Farm, Somerset: Developing a vineyard business alongside an existing smallholding with holiday cottage

The Southern Slopes Vineyard journey started in 2005 when James and Gill Cummings purchased a small run down farm close to Wells in Somerset. The south facing land was a mixture of rough grazing and scrubby coppice that had been neglected for many years. Although the idea for a vineyard came almost immediately they arrived, they spent the first four years farming a small flock of Suffolk sheep, raising rare-breed pigs and building up a holiday cottage business, and it was to be a further seven years before they planted their first vines.

Firstly the Cummings considered the type of business model: vineyard only, vineyard and winery, tasting room, tours, etc. For them the vineyard experience widened the appeal of the holiday cottage and added the potential for workshops, tastings, tours and wine sales. Even before they planted, they were thinking about how they would raise awareness of the vineyard and the wines, and used Twitter and Facebook to document the back-story of 'our vineyard journey'. James Cummings feels that "it is a good idea to take loads of photos and use them in a blog to keep followers up to date".

James's advice is not to underestimate the goodwill and support you will receive from local people who will quickly view it as their village vineyard! Make sure you acquire the knowledge you need to make a success of the project. For James this meant studying on a two-year viticulture, wine-production and wine business degree at Plumpton College, as well as studying with the WSET at advanced and diploma level. Further practical experience came from a work placement at Furleigh Estate in Dorset. On-going training has been provided by WineSkills in a range of subjects including master classes in canopy management, sparkling wine production and quality assurance, as well as workshops covering pruning, trunk disease and pesticide application. Meeting with local vineyard owners early on in the project helped James and Gill to clarify their aims.

Carry out detailed research, particularly on grape varieties suitable for your wine style, including clones and rootstocks best adapted to your site's soil conditions and mesoclimate. Study and model best practice from other cool-climate winegrowing regions.

James also advises that "if you are able to get a work placement in a vineyard make the most of it. Take photos and make notes on everything you are involved in. Not just what you did, but also the philosophy behind it and any ideas you might have for improvement. You will find the notes invaluable when you come to reflect on your own procedures".

He goes on to say "be realistic in your site evaluation, as a poorly located and prepared site will never provide the returns needed for a successful business". It is worth taking the time to benchmark your site against optimal values for the UK and other northern European wine regions. Consider, aspect, slope, soil type and structure and drainage characteristics. Take two or three soil samples from your site and send them to the Laverstoke Park laboratory for analysis, the report is incredibly detailed but makes sure you act on any priority recommendations".

"Consider planting windbreaks a year ahead of the vines and stock-proof, and even deer, fencing may be necessary. Access is important for machinery and materials. Don't underestimate the amount of work involved in site preparation, and equally don't be tempted to cut corners as this will result in more work in the long run."

James states that if you are used to working on the land you will be able to tackle many aspects of site preparation yourself. For larger jobs requiring specialist equipment, it makes sense to use the services of an experienced contractor. In their case this included digging out tree stumps on the sloping site, deep ripping, ploughing and power harrowing the whole area.

At Panniers Farm, the transformation of the site began three years before planting. Borrowing ideas from the conservation grazing approach to land management, James and Gill used their small herd of pigs to help clear the brambles and scrub. The area was then sown with chicory, rye grass and clover for the sheep to graze the following year. The process helps improve soil conditions, stimulates the grass to out-compete perennial weeds, and provides a small stream of income while the land is in transition.

Overgrown hazel hedges were cut down to ground level to stimulate strong re-growth, creating windbreaks. The boundary fencing was improved and deer fencing erected on the side bordering woodland. Soil preparation involved spraying off the vegetation and deep ripping, followed by ploughing and power harrowing. To improve soil structure and increase organic matter 200 tonnes of cow manure were spread, followed by a further harrowing.

James thought that it made sense to erect the trellis system before planting, as manoeuvring machinery on the slope would be tricky with young vines in place. The Geneva Double Curtain system used allowed them to plant at a lower density and to benefit from reduced shoot vigour, improved light interception and potentially higher yields. Materials for trellising cost significantly more than the vines themselves, so it is important to take care at the design and specification stage.

It is also worth mentioning that there is little confidence in the tantalising process with posts rotting off at ground level within five years. We suggest using pressure-treated creosote posts or galvanised metal posts if your budget allows. Their system, for the one-hectare site, required over 500 posts, cross members, bolts and timber joiners, with 62 earth anchors and 8500m of wire.

In their experience "your energy levels are highest in the period leading up to planting, so use this time to develop a plan for the first year's vineyard activity. Try to integrate it into your other activities on the farm and, above all, keep your followers and potential customers in the loop as the vineyard takes shape. This back-story will help build your profile and demand for your wines ahead of their release".

www.panniersfarm.co.uk

Food and drink festivals

Local food and drink festivals have grown in popularity across the country and are perfect places to introduce people to your wines, which can be purchased by the glass or the bottle. There may be an initial outlay for a stall, but this could be shared with another local winery to reduce costs. Cornwall, Kingston in Surrey, Manchester, Colchester, Nantwich, Exeter, Horsham, Ludlow and Bristol, to name only a few of the many throughout the country, hold local festivals. New Hall Vineyards, near Maldon, Essex **www.newhallwines.co.uk**, has a dedicated English Wine Festival and Open Day for two days in late summer. It includes children's activities, wine tastings and tours, local food, fire-eaters, trailer rides and local craft stalls. The website **www.localfoodadvisor.com** promotes local English and Welsh vineyards and wine, drink and food suppliers and producers, as well as food and farmers markets across the country. In addition, the **www.thefestivalcalendar.co.uk** website lists UK food and drink festivals free of charge.

"Food festivals are one of the most important ways for UK wineries to expose domestic consumers to English wine. Even in Sussex, an important wine-producing region of the south east, there is a huge lack of knowledge of local wines with the local population. Food festival events allow wineries to showcase their product to multiple demographics in terms of age, spend and wine knowledge. Intimate engagement between the business and the consumer, and the local hospitality industry, creates an important lasting impression that influences future wine purchasing. Brighton's food festival is unique, in that the organising committee consists of a group of volunteers from across the food and hospitality industry. Hence the commitment to promoting good, local food to residents and businesses spans not only the festival period but the entire year. Without a doubt, getting Sussex wines into more local retailers, bars and restaurants is a key objective of the organisation".

Nick Mosley, Brighton and Hove Food and Drink Festival Director
www.brightonfoodfestival.com

Weddings and civil ceremonies

Vineyards can be beautiful and magical settings for weddings and civil ceremonies, either as a location for the reception or the actual marriage as well. Full event strategy and planning is part of a strong business plan to maximise income from the vineyard. For wedding licences to perform marriages, you need to apply to the home office via the following link **www.homeoffice.gov.uk/publications/agencies-public-bodies/ips/general-ips-publications/civil-reg/guidance-approving-premises?view=Binary**. As a reception venue it is important to consider room capacity, changing facilities and marquee hire, and to gather a list of local flower arrangers, photographers, caterers and music providers to suit every need. It can be useful to work with local hotels if the vineyard does not have accommodation available on-site, and even to consider employing a specialised wedding coordinator to help with the organisation.

Art exhibitions

The visitors centre can also be used as an art exhibition space or for resident artists and craft fairs. It is also possible to use the UK countryside and the grounds of a vineyard to create an art gallery using natural materials and local artists, sculptors and school children to widen engagement with the community. Giffords Hall, Bury St Edmunds, Suffolk **www.giffordshall.co.uk** had a contemporary locally based, internationally recognised artist and a photographer exhibiting their work during their open weekend. Art work exhibited on the vineyard property can bring people to the vineyard that may otherwise not visit and after negotiation with the artist, the vineyard can earn commission from any art sold.

Leasing vines/Rent-a-vine/Adopt-a-vine schemes

Adopt-a-vine schemes are utilised by a number of UK vineyards such as Welcombe Hills, Stratford upon Avon, Warwickshire, **www.welcombehills.co.uk**, which gives people the opportunity to own a few vines or a whole row. The bearer can visit the vineyard at any time throughout the year (by prior arrangement), help with the harvest of the vines and is entitled to a 10 per cent discount on all purchases of Welcombe Hills wine for one year. Pebblebed Vineyard, Devon **www.pebblebedwines.co.uk**, has a similar scheme, and Chapel Down, Kent has an extensive lease-a-vine scheme **www.chapeldown.com**. Kent Vineyard, Colliers Green **www.kentvineyard.co.uk** is planning to launch a rent-a-vine scheme; Ryedale Vineyard, Yorkshire **www.ryedalevineyards.co.uk** has a similar scheme, as does Seddlescombe Organic Vineyard, East Sussex **www.englishorganicwine.co.uk**. These schemes increase income for the vineyard and can help secure grape pickers for the harvest. Wickham Vineyard, Hampshire **www.wickhamvineyard.com** has a wine scheme operated via **www.wineshare.co.uk**, and these types of schemes can also be purchased via online gift websites like **www.buyagift.co.uk**. All the schemes are different and purchasers receive different benefits, but a "Friends of the Vineyard" scheme can result in long term, loyal customers and additional regular annual income. It is important to have administrative assistance with these schemes and be confident that all the benefits of the scheme can be delivered successfully. Any vines in the scheme need to be marked on a vineyard map, then tagged in the vineyard with the name of the purchaser, and competitions, newsletters and discounts offered to scheme members. Regular contact must be maintained with members. Social network sites offer a good way to do this, as well as seasonal email updates. The crucial point to remember with any rent-a-vine scheme is to show to the purchaser that the scheme is value for money and benefits them, as well as the vineyard.

Concerts

Vineyard concerts, both small and large scale events, are extremely popular in many wine regions, especially in New World wine producing countries like Australia, USA and New Zealand. Concerts present a wonderful opportunity to sell your wine if you ban the bringing of alcohol into the event and ensure that the only alcohol on sale is the vineyard's own. Any concert would depend on the size of the vineyard, facilities and the type of music. With planning and organisation, and a band in a marquee, selling local food on a barbecue alongside local wine can be a successful income stream. Classical

Case study: Renishaw Hall, North Derbyshire: Kieron Atkinson

Revenue Streams

Renishaw Hall benefits from a tremendous history: the house itself dates back to 1625 and the vineyard was planted 40 years ago by the charismatic late Sir Reresby Sitwell, making it an impressive age for a UK vineyard. Kieron Atkinson took over the running of all wine-related business during the summer of 2011, and it was soon apparent that a number of quick wins could be implemented to increase revenue from the vineyard and wine sales. Renishaw Hall and Gardens already attract in the region of 20,000-30,000 visitors each year, but opportunities were not being taken to raise awareness of the vineyard and its wine to this key audience. His first action was to focus on how he could increase awareness of the vineyard and the wine, essentially a unique selling point of visiting Renishaw Hall, to people coming through the gate from April to October.

On-site marketing and visitor opportunities

Kieron wanted the staff and volunteers who worked onsite to support the wine and vineyard more than they had previously done. The aim was for them to realise the potential for the Hall as well as improving the visitor experience to Renishaw. He organised training days and tastings so that everyone could get to know the wine and gain their own opinion of it, and could talk to the public more confidently. He also put 'table talkers' and posters about the wine and forthcoming tours in the restaurant and shop, so that over a coffee or lunch visitors could sit and read about the vineyard (which had not been done previously). The shop layout has also improved immeasurably, and is still work in progress. He is also getting consultation from local retailers to sharpen what is presented in the Renishaw Hall shop and ensure they are getting the message across successfully.

Linked to this is the selling of other wine-related products such as wine labels as prints and postcards, which has been successfully done by other wine-producers, most famously by Mouton Rothschild. Sales of labels of course ultimately rest on the quality and interest of the labels, so he has designed new labels which feature striking images of Renishaw Hall

Gardens by Rex Whistler. Vineyard tours are also a revenue stream, but having tours available all day every day was not cost effective. Therefore he structured a package of tours for key months of the year to a minimum number of people. Based on 2011, the tours averaged around 60 visitors a day on two tours. Any more than this and fatigue can set in for the tour conductor, but also if the tours are too large visitors do not get such a good experience. Private tours are also available, and can be pre-booked for businesses. They make a great day out for groups, including personal tours, as well as more commercial groups such as restaurants and pub staff.

Regarding press and public relations, Kieron immediately volunteered his services for local press and PR as his previous army career makes for a good story: "swapping a rifle for secateurs". He conducted private wine tours and did interviews with the local papers and county magazines. The coverage in these publications had a direct impact on bookings for vineyard tours at the Hall as well as an increased interest in English wine. He aims to get media exposure for seasonal 'stories' in the vineyard, and the story of a Derbyshire vineyard and its great age makes the Renishaw Vineyard one that journalists are interested in.

Aside from visitors to the Hall and Gardens at Renishaw, Kieron's core business is the local market within an hour of the site. This incorporates the cities of Sheffield, Nottingham, Leeds, Derby and Manchester, and the tourists who visit the Peak District each year. He chose to get the wine on sale in the three best restaurants, delicatessens and hotels in the area. Not so much to generate a huge amount of sales, but to appear on the menus and on the shelves to raise awareness of the product.

www.sitwell.co.uk/vineyard

concerts, open-air theatre, local amateur dramatics, local band showcase and talent competitions are all ideas that can introduce different types of people to your vineyard and ultimately your wine. There would be an initial outlay for a marquee, in case of wet weather, and music (whether a full band or a single keyboard player), but these could be covered by charging food outlets for pitches and be reflected in the ticket price. Using free social media sites like a Facebook group, Twitter and local media to promote it, along with an email campaign to existing customers, will generate interest. A small-scale picnic or barbecue with jazz in the vineyard will obviously be cheaper to stage than a large-scale concert where a promotion company might be required. Joining with local companies, musicians, restaurants or music colleges can help. Consideration would need to be given to the time and duration of the event, but a Sunday afternoon amongst the vines with wine, food and music is always popular! Remember to organise the clearing up afterwards in advance, and stage the entire event at a safe distance from the actual vines.

Farms, cottages, bed and breakfast accommodation

Some vineyards are located on land with existing property that has been converted to earn extra income as a holiday cottage. Aller Hill Vineyard, Somerset **http://allerhill.blogspot.co.uk** converted a two-bedroomed 18th-century barn into a holiday cottage. Camel Valley Vineyard, Bodmin, Cornwall **www.camelvalley.com** has two holiday cottages to let. Tiltridge Farm, Severn Valley, Worcestershire **www.elgarwine.com**, which produces Elgar wine, offers bed and breakfast accommodation in their farmhouse, as does Denbies Estate, Surrey. Holiday cottages can provide a second income revenue for vineyards, but if there is not an existing property on the prospective vineyard land or there is a dilapidated property that needs converting, then considerably more expense and time will be incurred on building work, regulations and planning consent.

Business courses and conferences

Many vineyards offer a venue for business courses and seminars, and Chilford Hall Vineyard, near Cambridge **www.chilfordhall.co.uk**

has one of the largest exhibition, conference and banqueting centres in the East of England, as well as a 20-acre vineyard. They offer banqueting for up to 700 people, conference facilities for up to 500 delegates, meeting facilities for up to 750 individuals, weddings in three separate venues for up to 500 guests, 2,600-square metres of exhibition space, 15 acres of grounds for outdoor events, winery tours and tastings, a wine shop and bistro, onsite parking for up to 1,000 cars, and even a helicopter landing area! Denbies Estate, Surrey, hosted the International Sparkling Wine Symposium in 2009 and 2011, and organises themed evenings, murder mystery weekends and many other specialised events. This scale of facilities requires a large financial input and must be part of a sales and marketing strategy. This is not always feasible or necessary if your priority is to produce high-quality wine, or for small vineyards. However, hospitality facilities of any type and size, with careful planning and organisation, can increase income and brand awareness.

Harvest parties

Post-harvest party celebrations occur in vineyards and wineries around the world, but in the UK these are often reserved exclusively for vineyard and winery staff (sometimes grape pickers), but could be extended to the wider local community. An annual harvest party for local people, with local food for sale, entertainment and the vineyard's own wine available, can increase local awareness of the brand, gather home grown support by encouraging brand loyalty and, if an entrance fee is charged, can increase revenue. Alternatively an annual harvest party could also be reserved for "Rent-a-Vine" members or "Friends of the Vineyard" members only. The contribution of these types of activities to building relationships with the local community and increasing income is often under estimated.

Friends of the vineyard schemes

A membership scheme that is common in the UK arts world, especially theatres and art galleries, could be transferred to vineyards, and that is a local "Friends" scheme, currently under-utilised by UK vineyards and wineries. These schemes could be adopted at a local level, and tailored to individual business requirements, to increase income and brand awareness. It would require administrative organisation, but could provide event volunteers, grape pickers for harvest, increase revenue and local brand loyalty, and even be purchased as gifts for wine-lovers. "Friends" could benefit from invitations to exclusive events, seasonal newsletters from the vineyard / winery, discounts on wine tastings, advance wine sales, discount on facility hire, invitations to wine auctions, discount in the onsite restaurant or a renowned local eatery. The scheme could be organised as a single or joint membership, in tiers with gold, silver and bronze memberships, or in conjunction with a local wine club or shop.

Community vineyards

Community vineyards and urban grapevine growing is increasing in popularity in the UK, with Forty Hall Community Vineyards, Lewisham Organic Vineyard and Warden Abbey Community Vineyard in Bedfordshire **www.wardenwines.co.uk** growing grapevines for local wine. Warden Abbey Vineyard had a new lease of life in 2012 and is now managed by, and for, the local community. These projects do not have wineries attached to them, so may require contract winemakers to produce their wines. If there is a local community vineyard in your area you may wish to consider contacting them with regards to offering your wine-production facilities for small-scale winemaking.

Chapter Seven

Finance

Case Studies

Finance

It is an old and well-used cliché to say that to make a small fortune in the wine trade you need to start with a big one, but it does ring true. Many are seduced by the idea of investing in wine, planting a vineyard, making their own wine, and, whilst some succeed, many fall by the wayside. The wine business, like any other business, requires investment, knowledge, financial acumen and hard work. Planting a vineyard is essentially farming, winemaking is industrial processing, and selling wine is a combination of marketing, and the retail and wholesale trades. Wine being the product of those activities can make it a pleasurable process at times, but this doesn't take away from the need to keep an eye on the bottom line.

How much money will you need to make your wine? To overuse yet another cliché – you might as well ask how long is a piece of string. There are so many variables, and you can become involved in the wine industry on so many levels – it really depends on how much of the process you want to take on yourself and on what scale. The industry in the UK is developing rapidly, with more qualified consultants and suppliers coming into the market. It is therefore almost impossible to give accurate figures for these costs; any costings will be out of date before this book can be published. Remember that the UK is a tiny market for most of the suppliers you will be working with. Your choices will be limited to those companies who are prepared to even contemplate doing business in the UK. Some will flatly turn you down. Thus, you will not have the bargaining power of a Champagne or Loire Valley winemaker when it comes to negotiating price. Also, it is worth remembering that if you ask a supplier for a complicated quote for thermo-regulation, tanks, etc. then take the information he has spent hours compiling for you and try to go to his competitors, word will get round, and you might find that original supplier will no longer wish to work with you. This may seem alien to the UK mindset of doing business, and may very well be illegal under EU law, but be aware that the winery and vineyard supply businesses all tend to know each other, and it pays to keep your suppliers happy.

We are useful to them as a safety-valve market, but we are certainly not integral to their business. You will get further with goodwill than hard-nosed haggling.

This is not to suggest that you should be prepared to be ripped off – just go into negotiations with a firm dose of reality: it costs money for them to do business in the UK, and you will not get the same prices open to larger winemaking regions.

Planting a vineyard, building and equipping a winery, selling the resulting wine – all of these are separate businesses within themselves. You can merely grow and sell grapes; buy grapes and make wine; or buy bulk wines to bottle and sell. There are now some 'virtual winemakers' entering the UK market; they own no vines, do not have a winery but 'create' a label or brand under which to sell. These guys are buying grapes and having a contract winemaker produce the wine, without ever having to get their own hands dirty in the field. It is a common business model in more established, most-often New World regions such as California. The risk is minimal - if there is a poor vintage with low yields, they only pay for the grapes they receive, whilst the vine-grower has still incurred the same costs in running their acreage, thus receiving a reduced income. Similarly, the winery taking the grapes under contract has to have capacity for the full projected yield (investment in tank space and other kit) but, again, if yields are low then the winery's revenue will be reduced. The biggest risk a virtual winemaker faces is not being able to sell his or her wine, and building a brand without having a place such as a vineyard or winery to pin it on can be tough.

You've decided on your wine style or styles. The costs are going to be determined by this – sparkling wine requires much more capital investment than still wine, and requires a longer period of patience before you will realise any potential return.

English still wines, selling at £10+ per bottle, are still perceived as expensive. By contrast, sparkling wine at £20 can look good value next to Champagne. The average retail price paid for still wine (from any country) was around the £4-5 mark. Bearing in mind that nearly half of that is duty and VAT – there is not much room for a small-scale producer to make a profit. To persuade the consumer to more than double their average spend to buy an English still wine is a long shot. For this reason still wines are always going to have a limited market – restricted to those consumers who are adventurous and prepared to spend a bit more money.

Sparkling wine, on the other hand, is viewed entirely differently: as a special occasion wine. The normal self-imposed restrictions on price paid are removed, and the consumer will pay much more for the perceived quality of English Sparkling Wine. Some basic research online and at Waitrose will show you what prices are currently achieved by English wines. All your costs are higher for sparkling, including duty, but the financial rewards can be higher still if you have the capital to invest for several years before you realise them.

Financial help available

There are various sources of funding, agricultural subsidies and business grants that are available to potential vineyard and winery owners. The coalition government cut off the South East England Development Agency (SEEDA), a body (part of the RDPE) that had given enormous help to the fledging English wine industry, and disbanded it in 2011. There are many many vineyards and wineries in the UK that would never have got off the ground without the matched grant funding from SEEDA, and many others, already established, that have upgraded their facilities and subsequently the quality of their wines after benefiting from the grants. This shortsightedness on the part of a government desperate to increase economic activity, in one of the few growing and vibrant rural industries the UK has, is depressing. But there are other avenues for funding if you look hard enough.

Although the SEEDA / RDPE funding has been cut off, it would be worth keeping in touch with DEFRA to be sure you don't miss out on any new grants that come on-stream.

As a farmer you might be entitled to the Single Farm Payment Scheme – contact the Rural Payments Agency on 0845 603 7777 or CSC@rpa.gsi.gov.uk to find out your eligibility. More information can be sourced on **www.rpa.defra.gov.uk**.

Business Link is a very good place to start – your local office will be able to help you with a business review, plus they should be able to point you towards any local and national grants available for new and/or small businesses that are not necessarily rural-based.

HMRC Notice 163 is a mine of information on your VAT, tax and duty liabilities as a wine producer.

The Prince of Wales not only operates his Prince's Trust for business grants and loans for under 30s, but he also has a lesser-known rural funding scheme: The Prince's Countryside Fund **http://princescountrysidefund.org.uk**. There are quite tight criteria in terms of giving back to the rural community in terms of amenities and jobs, but at least one vineyard is applying for the funding. The goals of the charity are:

- To improve the sustainability of British farming and rural communities, targeting the areas of greatest need
- To reconnect consumers with countryside issues
- To support farming and rural crisis charities through a dedicated emergency funding stream

So, any project has to meet at least one of these criteria, and Amber Valley Wines in Derbyshire has teamed up with Renishaw Estate, Mercian Vineyard Assciation and the National Trust at Hardwick Hall to submit an application. Their project aims to partner with local farmers to look at diversifying their land into vineyards, giving young people jobs and training them in winemaking and vine-growing. In an area where mining was the key industry, regeneration with the help of the Prince's Fund could revitalise the area.

There are, of course, always commercial loan and mortgage companies who operate and specialise in the rural and farming industries, one example, although by no means the only option, is **www.farmfunding.co.uk**.

The costs of a vineyard

Agricultural land in the UK is much cheaper than in the classic, established wine regions. For comparison, a hectare of vineyard land in the Champagne region will change hands for 1 million euros, a hectare of Napa Valley vineyard will cost US$250,000, whilst a hectare of suit-

Case study: Chapel Down: the English Wines Group

Chapel Down is one of the older vineyards and wineries in the UK, based at Tenterden in Kent. Started in the 1970s making predominantly still wines the company has shifted its focus to sparkling wine in recent years. One way it has managed its expansion to becoming one of the biggest wineries in England is by emulating the New Zealand and Champagne models of not only running their own vineyards (about 30% of production) but also partnering with other vineyards with long term contracts to provide quality grapes. These partner vineyards are located in Kent and further afield. By guaranteeing to buy the grapes produced from the vineyards (subject to quality criteria being met), Chapel Down gives the landowners the incentive and confidence to plant, in the knowledge that they will get guidance on establishment and growing from an experienced team. Chapel Down gets to expand its production significantly without the massive investment required to acquire land and also spreads the risk of a bad harvest across several locations. The growers are given financial incentives to up the quality of their fruit and Chapel Down only has to pay out per ton of grapes produced rather than having to maintain vineyards on a cost per acre basis.

In 2004 the Managing Director of Chapel Down Group, Frazer Thompson, made the decision to float the company on the PLUS market. PLUS is an alternative to the London Stock Exchange and AIM (Alternative Investment Market) for smaller companies looking to raise money by selling shares to investors. Current share prices for Chapel Down Group hover around £0.15 with a low of £0.125 and a high of £0.16 in 2011. It is not looking likely to make any of the investors a huge fortune just yet, but the funds raised from doing this allowed the company to upgrade its winery and increase production, particularly in the capital-heavy sparkling wine side of the business. The long-term nature of the investment in winemaking means that investors could still see a healthy return on their investment over the next few years as the winery builds up stock and the increase in the selling price of the wines which has risen hugely since the flotation. In addition, being publicly floated gives the business a transparency and integrity that inspires confidence from their supermarket clients, a factor that is increasingly important in the competitive wine market.

The vineyard and winery team is made up of a dedicated group from across the globe as well home-grown Plumpton graduates. Andrew Parley, from New Zealand, is ably assisted by Englishman Josh Donaghy-Spire in the winery whilst the vineyard team manages both the estate vineyards and advises all the out-lying contract growers.

This route to raising funds is not an option for a newcomer in reality. That Chapel Down had decades of winemaking history to back up its business plan will have been a big factor in the confidence of investors. By floating publicly the ownership of the company is diluted so wouldn't appeal to many landowners or farmers, where ownership of the land is crucial. But the model of encouraging partner vineyards is perfectly plausible for new entrants into the industry.

www.chapeldown.com

able land in the UK might only cost £20,000. Farmers and landowners who have suitable sites for vineyards in the South of England are probably going to wise up to the fact that a sheltered, south-facing, free-draining slope at less than 100 metres above sea level is a fairly rare commodity, and will no doubt start asking for more money. Strutt and Parker is a firm of estate agents that has taken an interest in vineyard-suitable land, having brokered many of the deals for Nyetimber's recent expansion across the South. They are involved with many new projects and the sale of existing vineyards **www.struttandparker.com**.

Soil-sampling is vital when considering purchase of a new site, and there are consultants who can do this for you. Look to pay for their time (up to £250 per day) plus any laboratory fees for the actual testing. The first site you look at might not prove suitable, and you will need to repeat the exercise. The cost of testing soil samples will vary according to the number of different samples. Prices can be requested from laboratories such as FAST **www.fastltd.co.uk**.Companies such as Vine-works **www.vine-works.com** and Vineyard Consulting **www.vineyardconsulting.co.uk** will undertake site assessments for a fee, to be negotiated according to location and size of the potential plot.

Once you've made your purchase of land you will need to prepare the soil for planting. You could hire a local farmer to do the preparation for you, or rent a tractor and the ploughing and harrowing equipment. You will never need a large tractor again once the vines are in, so it is not cost-effective to purchase a tractor or the equipment for this, unless you have one as part of a larger operation anyway.

Deer and rabbit fencing is almost obligatory in the UK if you want your baby vines to survive beyond their first year. Again, how much this will cost will depend on the size of the area you wish to protect. Rabbits can also be prevented with grow-tubes – these also offer some protection against frost for young vines. Vine guards can cost £0.50 each.

Planting can be done by a contractor on specialist machines and costs would vary according to location and size of site/number of vines. Ernst Weis from Germany is the current go-to guy for planting by machine, but you do need to get in early. And there is not much room for negotation on price, seeing as he is the only one with the equipment and skilled workers to do it. If you do it by hand you will need a large team of people and know that they will do it properly.

The summer following the planting will see the need for trellising to be installed. This again will vary enormously in cost according to size, plus you need to take into account your soil type. If you have solid chalk at 20cm below the surface, it will cost more to drive the posts in, and you may need sturdier posts at a higher cost as well.

You should budget for £20,000 per hectare on top of of the price of the land, to get established with vines and trellising. This should also cover maintenance and labour for the first two years before the vineyard becomes productive.

Selling/purchasing your grapes

If you decide that you just want to be a grape-grower, then you can sell your grapes as a cash crop. Alternatively, you might wish to enter the market at this point and buy grapes from a vine-grower. Historically, the classic three Champagne varieties of Chardonnay, Pinot noir and Pinot meunier fetch the highest prices. Starting at around £1,500 per ton, the actual price paid can go down if good ripeness is not achieved, and up if a better balance between sugar and acidity is realised. The better vineyards, with a track record of producing well-balanced fruit, will charge closer to £2,000 per ton, with some chancing their arm in 2011 (a very small yielding vintage) at well over £2,000 per ton.

Growers of still wine varieties can expect a lot less for their grapes. Bacchus retains a fairly healthy price, and could fetch up to £1,200 per ton for good-quality fruit in a low-yielding year of short supply, but other still varieties might only achieve £800 per ton.

Tread carefully when purchasing fruit – some growers take umbrage at a sliding scale being offered based on ripeness, and don't necessarily understand that this is how grapes are sold the world over. Likewise, if you are the grower, realise that taking action in the vineyard to increase quality can result in higher prices per ton, cancelling out any perceived loss of income from reduced yield. Also,

Case study: Hambledon Vineyard: an unusual route to raising funds

Hambledon Vineyard in Hampshire boasts a long and distinguished history in English winemaking. The first truly commercial vineyard and winery in England, planted by Major-General Sir Guy Salisbury-Jones in 1952, past vintages of Hambledon wines have been served in British embassies across the world and in the Houses of Parliament. The current owner, Ian Kellett, has big ambitions for the business, and has gone about raising the necessary investment through a number of unique ways. He has owned the property since 1999, and in the following ten years he replanted the vineyard with the three major Champagne grape varieties: Chardonnay, Pinot noir and Pinot meunier. Until the 2010 vintage, he sold the entire crop to other wine-producers across the country. In 2010 Kellett launched a campaign to raise £4 million through the tax-efficient Enterprise Investment Scheme (EIS). The minimum investment was £10,000, attracting private investors to fund expansion of the current acreage and develop the new winery, its equipment and future sales.

The current land-holding of 23 acres, of which ten were planted, was added to by leasing 33 acres of adjacent land in 2011 and, following the success of the EIS scheme, ground was broken for a new winery extension for pressing and fermentation, extending the existing winery building. This is now the fourth generation of winery on the site.

Hambledon was also recipient of a record sum (more than £500,000) from SEEDA (South East England Development Agency), who granted funds contingent on the EIS being successful. SEEDA no longer exists as of 2011, one of the many victims of the current coalition government's funding cuts, see above.

The result is a new winery with a small initial volume of wine being produced on site from 2011. Hervé Jestin, a consultant from Champagne (where he was previously Chef de Caves of Duval-Leroy for 20 years), is responsible for over-seeing the winemaking, and leads the winemaking team with Antoine Arnault, a French winemaker. Kellett is joined by non-executive directors John Armit, a veteran of the London wine trade,

Andrew Christie-Miller and Martin Robinson. The details of the EIS Prospectus that was issued to prospective investors very rightly point out the highly risky nature of investing in such a venture. By spreading this risk over a wider pool of investors, the directors themselves are able to reduce their own exposure in what is a notoriously fickle industry.

Ian Kellett has a background in food technology, and still works full time in the City in this area. Recognising the need for wine industry-specific knowledge, the day-to-day running of the winery is in the hands of Antoine Arnault and Hervé Jestin, whilst the work in the vineyard is run by Peter Crabtree, who has been looking after the site for many years.

This is a very ambitious project within what is still a tiny industry, and this route to establishment is not open to many people. The industry (and no doubt the investors) will be watching and waiting to see whether this bold strategy has paid off.

Hambledon Vineyard Plc, The Vineyard, Hambledon, Hampshire PO7 4RY,
info@hambledonvineyard.co.uk
www.hambledonvineyard.co.uk

achieving better-quality grapes year on year will mean that you will have the track record to maintain a higher price when supply of grapes inevitably increases.

The UK industry is in a state of flux, and grapes are in relatively short supply at the moment. Looking at recent planting figures this will not be the case forever and, whilst the shoe is firmly on the foot of the grower at the moment, it is likely to move to the purchaser's foot as more and more vineyards compete for the same buyers.

The costs of making the wine

If you are making traditional method, bottle-fermented sparkling wine you will be making wine and squirrelling it away for nearly three years before you even attempt to sell any. Therefore, any winemaking cost calculations need to take this pause in any return into account.

The direct costs of making wine are the grapes, yeast, additions such as sugar, a bottle, a closure and the label. All other costs are overheads such as utilities, labour and capital expenditure on equipment. Just taking those direct costs can make winemaking an attractive proposition. However, the overheads can be huge and uncontrolled, and can far outweigh any potential return.

Example (a still wine):

- £1,000 per ton of grapes might yield 900 bottles, making the grape cost £1.11 per bottle –growing your own grapes means you can hopefully reduce this figure
- Yeast and other additions for the same 900 bottles might be £3.00 in total
- Sugar to chaptalise/enrich by 2 per cent would cost around £20.00 or £0.02 per bottle
- The bottle itself could be anything from £0.35 to £0.50 depending on weight, style, quality
- A cork can vary in price from £0.15 to £0.25, again depending on quality
- A plain capsule will be less than £0.03, whilst branded ones will be more

- Label costs are also difficult to quantify and can vary hugely
- The total cost will be at least £2.00 if you go for the cheapest of everything; and quite likely more

This does not take into account the labour, the power required, interest on capital expenditure, interest paid on loans and boxes for final packaging.

Example (a sparkling wine):

- Grapes for sparkling are more expensive and yield a lower volume of juice so £1,750 per ton might only yield 800 bottles at a cost of £2.19 per bottle equivalent
- Yeast, and other other additions such as sugar for chaptalisation, would be similar to still wine
- The bottles are heavier and therefore more expensive, starting at £0.50 per bottle for bulk orders and as much as £0.75 or more for smaller orders
- Crown caps and bidules at tirage (bottling), along with more yeast and additions, would be £0.05-8 per bottle
- Storage for a minimum 9 months and more likely several years – cost at a specialist facility would be £0.20-30 per bottle
- The cork and wire at disgorging would add another £0.25 plus £0.07
- Foils, labels and boxes are all dependent on type and style
- With more variables in terms of storage length, etc. sparkling wine could cost at least £3.50 per bottle before accounting for labour and power

Getting the label right, as well as the foil and other packaging, can involve a branding agency, focus groups, graphic desginers, marketing consultants, etc. – all before you've even got to the type of paper and printer – and it can cost a fortune. There are specialist packaging suppliers such as Sparflex **www.sparflex.com** – who have an office in the UK – who will do the whole design process (from a brief supplied by you) for a few thousand euros, as long as you get them to print and produce the labels.

Selling your wine

If you sell your wine direct to the consumer you will make the highest margin and the greatest gross profit – however, it might not be the most efficient way of selling. Taking on a distributor might seem unnecessary and reduce the margin that you can achieve, but once you are producing a significant volume you may not be able to sell all your stock from the cellar door, or manage the sales by yourself. It is easy to overlook the cost of your own time that might be better spent in the winery or vineyard, and how do you quantify the cost of the sales you have missed because you didn't have representation in the market?

Hiring a dedicated sales team or person is another option that probably isn't worth considering until you are producing hundreds of thousands of bottles. A good distributor will do all the legwork for you and has a sales team already working across the country. This is worth the reduced margin you will get by selling to them.

See Chapter 5 for more details on marketing.

Appendix: Customs and Duty

NOTICE 163 WINE PRODUCTION (FEBRUARY 2012) - SUMMARY

Notice 163 explains the law and regulations covering, production, storage, and accounting for duty on wine and made-wine. The law and regulations covering the handling of wine in Excise warehouses are explained in Notice 196 and Notice 197. The main legal provisions relating to the production, holding and movement of wine are in the Alcoholic Liquor Duties Act 1979 and the Wine and Made-wine Regulations 1989. For the complete Nortice visit www.hmrc.gov.uk.

Other legislation applying to wine producers includes the Customs & Excise Management Act 1979, the Revenue Traders (Accounts & Records) Regulations 1992, which cover the keeping of records, the Excise Goods (Holding, Movement & Duty Point) Regulations 2010 which cover the intra-Community movement and storage of goods, and the Excise Goods (Drawback) Regulations 1995. You can get copies from the Office of Public Sector Information.

Wine

The Alcoholic Liquor Duties Act defines wine as liquor of a strength exceeding 1.2% ABV made by fermentating fresh grapes (or the must of fresh grapes), whether or not the liquor is fortified with spirits or flavoured with aromatic extracts.

Made-wine is liquor of a strength exceeding 1.2% ABV made by fermenting any substance, or by mixing a liquor so obtained (or derived from a liquor so obtained) with any other liquor or substance except wine, beer, spirits or cider. Made-wine, for example, will include products similar to wine but not made from fresh grape, and some ready to drink alcoholic products (RTDs).

Sparkling wine is wine carbonated to at least three bars and packaged in a bottle closed by a mushroom cork and cage.

Premises

Excise-licenced premises

To make and sell wine, you normally need to get an Excise licence for your premises by completing form L5 and send it with entry of your premises to:

HM Revenue & Customs National Registration Unit (Alcohol and Tobacco)
Portcullis House
21 India Street
Glasgow G2 4PZ
(Tel: 0141 555 3489/3586)

Your licence allows you to:

- produce wine on your premises
- store your own wine in duty suspense

- receive wine in duty suspense from other winemakers for further processing eg bottling, and
- receive back in duty suspense your own product after processing by other winemakers.

Your Excise licence does not allow you to receive beer, cider, spirits, or imported wine.

A separate licence is required for each premises where you intend to make wine. However you may submit a single duty return for all licensed premises owned by the same legal entity (company, sole trader etc).

As part of your licence application you must "make entry" of premises, ie supply a plan showing the position and description of each vessel or other piece of plant. It should include any identifying marks on the vessels or plant and should be submitted to the HMRC National Registration Unit with the completed L5.

Your licence will last until you cease production. You must notify HMRC in writing of any changes that may affect your licence, including ceasing production, a change of licensee, production of other dutiable goods on the premises, or financial difficulties. A change of ownership requires a new L5 and entry of premises.

An on-site shop or restaurant is not considered part of the registered premises. Any wine sold in the shop or restaurant must be duty-paid on removal from the registered part of the premises.

Growers who don't have their own winery can send their grapes to a licensed maker to be vinified. If the resulting wine is for their own consumption duty is not payable. If the wine is for sale, the duty should be paid by the contract winemaker. Alternatively, to help cash-flow, growers can take out their own Excise licence and pay the duty themselves.

Trade facility warehouses

A trade facility warehouse is an Excise warehouse approved under the Customs & Excise Management Act 1979. You will need a trade facility warehouse approval, in addition to your winery licence, if you wish to receive and store duty free spirits for fortifying, or beer, cider or imported wine for use in the production of wine or made-wine.

HMRC will restrict any approval as a trade facility warehouse to the specific trade need detailed on your application. For further details on approval of premises and HMRC requirements, see Notice 196.

You may be required to provide a secure compartment for the storage of dutiable materials. The entrance door and any approved compartments must be secured in accordance with the requirements for warehousing premises. To have part of your winery approved as a trade facility warehouse, you will be required to obtain a financial guarantee.

The deposit of goods in a trade facility warehouse is governed by the Excise Warehousing (Etc.) Regulations 1988 (SI 1988/809). Any Customs duty due on imported materials to be used in the production of wine must have been accounted for before receipt into the trade facility warehouse.

You must keep a record of all receipts and usage of goods deposited in warehouse.

You may fortify wine in your trade facility warehouse if it has been produced in your winery, or received from another winery without payment of duty. Fortification is governed by EC Regulations which are administered by the Department for Environment Food & Rural Affairs. It may be necessary to consult Defra before we can approve your application. You can fortify wine or made-wine with added alcohol provided the final strength of the fortified wine or made-wine does not exceed 22% ABV.

Duty

Calculating and paying Duty

Duty is charged in bands determined by the alcoholic strength (% ABV) stated on the package label or invoice. It becomes payable when wine is released from or consumed in Excise-licensed premises or Excise warehouses or on removal from duty suspense.

To calculate and pay the duty you must:

- keep records of all wine produced
- keep records of all wine leaving licensed premises or otherwise passing the duty point
- calculate duty due on all wine released for UK home market use
- keep records of all wine destroyed
- complete a monthly duty return and send it to the Central Collection Unit, and
- pay the duty by the due date by one of the stipulated methods.
- The duty rates for wine are stated as amounts per hectolitre, and the current rates are on www.hmrc.gov.uk. There are six bands for wine and made-wine:
- wine/made-wine 1.2-4% ABV
- wine/made-wine 4-5.5% ABV
- still wine/made-wine 5.5-15% ABV
- still wine/made-wine 15-22% ABV (Wines exceeding 22% ABV are rated as spirits).
- sparkling wine 5.5-8.5% ABV
- sparkling wine 8.5-15% ABV.

For duty purposes, alcohol by volume should be truncated to one decimal place so that, for example, 5.59% ABV becomes 5.5% ABV. You can use any method to measure the strength as long as it produces results consistent with those that would be achieved using the distillation analysis or reference method preferred by HMRC. However, you must be prepared to explain your method, and an independent analyst must test the ABV of each of your products at least annually. The results of the independent analyses must be held in your business records.

HMRC will usually accept for duty purposes the strength declared on the package label, invoice, delivery note or similar document, but if you use the declared strength for duty purposes you must be able to show that you have continually monitored and recorded your ABV results so that, on average, the actual ABV of each finished product equates to what you are declaring.

If there is a dispute over the strength HMRC may analyse samples using the reference method. The analysis result will establish the dutiable strength of the wine for legal purposes.

Duty becomes payable when the wine passes the duty point, that is when it leaves the Excise-licensed premises, unless it is going to other approved premises for processing, to an Excise warehouse, for export, or to some specialised destinations such as HM ships or entitled diplomats. Normally, duty should be paid by the 15th day following the end of the accounting period in which the wine passed the duty point.

Financial guarantees

First-time producers must supply a financial guarantee, normally from their bank, sufficient to cover any outstanding duty unless they are eligible to make payments without guarantee under the Excise Payment Security System (EPSS). To be eligible for EPSS you must have been VAT-registered for three years or more. If you are trading beneath the VAT registration threshold, you can still apply for EPSS if you have been registered in an excise payment regime for three years or more. Alternatively, you can pay a year's estimated duty in advance.

If a guarantee is required, you must apply in writing to:

HM Revenue & Customs National Registration Unit (Approvals Team)
Portcullis House
21 India St
Glasgow G2 4PZ.

To apply for EPSS, complete an application form EPSS(B) which can be or obtained from the Excise & Customs Helpline on 0845 010 9000 and send the completed application form to:

EPSS Authorisation Team
Ruby House
8 Ruby Place
Aberdeen AB10 1ZP

Enforcement

HMRC will make visits to make sure duty is being correctly assessed and accounted for. It will carry out physical checks on production, stock and movements of wine in duty suspension. Officers will normally make a prior appoint ment. Occasionally, they may visit without appointment but the attending officer will give the reason. At any reasonable time you must permit officers access to any area of the premises, and all staff should be aware of this. All officers will show identification when they arrive. You should keep the Excise licence on the premises to which it refers.

If you fail to comply with the law and regulations relating to this notice or do not account for the correct amount of duty, HMRC can issue assessments and/or civil penalties. These are explained in Notice 208 and Notice 209. You may also be liable to penalties if you fail to apply to register with HMRC or if your monthly duty return is inaccurate.

If you fail to pay the duty by the due date, you will be liable to a civil penalty of 5% of the duty or £250, whichever is greater. In addition, further penalties may be incurred for each day that you fail to pay the duty. Details of civil penalties are contained in Notice 209.

At any time after the due date for payment, HMRC may take action to take possession of all wine, and all materials and equipment used in making wine or connected with your trade as a wine producer, whether these are your property or not, and auction them to recover duty due plus pay distraint costs.

When HMRC makes a decision you can appeal against, it should inform you and offer you a review. If you disagree with one of its decisions you usually have three options. Within 30 days you can send new information or arguments to the officer you have been dealing with, have your case reviewed by a different officer, or have your case heard by an independent tribunal. If you want HMRC to review a decision, it should complete its review within 45 days. If you are not satisfied with the review's conclusion, you have another 30 days to ask a tribunal to hear your case. You can find further information about reviews and appeals in fact sheet HMRC1 HMRC Decisions – What to do if you disagree. You can get this fact sheet at **www.hmrc.gov.uk** or by phoning the Orderline on 0845 900 0404.

Accounting for and paying duty

At the end of each accounting period, that is calendar month, or four- or five-week period agreed beforehand with HMRC, you must total up all the wine sent out from your premises during that period, work out the duty due, complete a duty account and transfer the appropriate totals to monthly return EX606. EX606s are routinely sent out to all licensed wine producers. If you fail to receive a return, you should contact the Central Collection Unit.

You must fill in your monthly duty return with:

- the quantity of wine in each relative duty band you sent out for home-use (or constructively removed) during the previous accounting period
- any allowable deductions, and
- the amount of duty you owe.

If you foresee any problems, you should immediately contact the:

HMRC Central Collection Unit (TAPS), 21 Victoria Avenue

Southend-on-Sea SS99 1AS, Phone: 01702 366558

If you have more than one licensed premises owned by the same legal entity, you may, on request, combine the duty liability for each in the one duty return. However, an individual duty summary should be maintained for each site and consolidated in a duty account by the site submitting the return. If you are approved to produce both cider and wine/made-wine, or if you produce either product on more than one set of premises, you may, as above, combine the duty liability for both products and /or premises in the one duty return.

If you deliberately make a false duty return, you may face prosecution for the offence and incur a heavy penalty. You have the right to appeal if HMRC imposes such a penalty.

If you discover underdeclarations relating to previous accounting periods which total less than £1,000 duty, you must enter the amounts on the reverse of the EX606 as appropriate, and carry the total forward to the current accounting period. Similarly, if you discover overdeclarations totalling less than £1,000 duty, you must enter the amounts on the reverse of the EX606 as appropriate and carry the total forward to the current accounting period. You do not have to send written advice, but details of the errors must be retained for inspection. If however, the total underdeclaration and/or overdeclaration is £1,000 duty or more, you must, in addition to making the adjustments outlined above, send full details in writing to the Central Collection Unit (TAPS).

You must submit your return and payment so that they arrive not later than the 15th of the month following the accounting period. When the 15th falls at a weekend or on a public holiday the return and payment must be received by the previous working day.

HMRC accepts payment by a range of methods but recommends you pay electronically using Bacs Direct Credit, CHAPS, or Internet or telephone banking.

Even if you make no deliveries of wine to home-use during an accounting period, you must still complete an EX606 return. Insert 'nil' in the quantities box, sign the return and send it in the normal way.

Duty reliefs – general information

Natural losses and wastage and other legitimate causes for lost product are not liable to duty provided HMRC is satisfied that they are genuine losses that are down to the production process.

There is also provision for duty relief on:

- accidental losses on licensed production premises
- spoilt wine or wine otherwise unfit for use
- wine not exceeding 1.2% ABV
- trade samples
- wine for your own domestic consumption.

Spillage and spoilage in Excise-licensed premises

Your records should indicate how much wine you lose during routine operations such the spillage you normally incur during packaging. Similarly, if duty suspended wine is spoilt you do not have to pay the duty providing HMRC is satisfied that the wine was unintentionally spoilt, contaminated, or otherwise rendered unfit for consumption while in the Excise-licensed premises and has not been consumed. You can write off the quantities concerned after you have recorded the information and destroyed any spoilt product.

For both accidental losses and spoilage you must record:

- the date and time the loss occurred
- the description (product name) and the volume of wine lost, and the alcoholic strength if the loss occurred after production had been completed
- the vessels in which it was contained, and
- the reason why the loss or spoilage occurred.

If wine cannot be accounted for after the start of production, and there is no acceptable explanation, you are liable for duty on the missing wine. If HMRC is not satisfied with your explanation and supporting evidence it will require you to pay the duty on the quantity written off.

Normally there is no duty relief in respect of wine lost after it has passed the duty point.

Destroying duty-suspended wine

You must give HMRC at least two working days' notice if you wish to destroy duty suspended wine on your own premises, or five working days' notice if the wine is to be destroyed elsewhere. You must give details of the proposed method of destruction and satisfy HMRC that your proposed process will destroy the intrinsic nature of the wine.

You must report:

- why you wish to destroy the goods
- details of the goods
- the amount of duty involved
- where and when the proposed destruction will take place, and
- the proposed method of destruction.

If the wine is removed from your premises to a specialist destruction site, there must be a complete audit trail which confirms that the wine has been destroyed. The process must be supervised by either your own Authorised Company Representative (ACR) or a person within the specialist destruction company who you have appointed to supervise the destruction on your behalf. This person must be at management or supervisory level, and a Certificate must be obtained from the company as evidence of destruction.

Duty refund on wine returned after spoilage

Wine which you have removed from your licensed premises on payment of duty may later become unfit for use. You can claim a refund provided the wine has not undergone any further process or dilution since it left your premises. Adulterated wine (that is, wine containing additions which HMRC has not approved), wine for which no satisfactory audit trail is available, and wine that is more than three years old are not eligible for a refund.

Spoilt wine may be either destroyed (see above) or reprocessed. Reprocessing includes the blending of the wine with another (or others) on Excise-licensed premises, and the filtering or repasteurising of the wine.

You must keep a spoiled wine record. When wine is returned to your premises either for destruction or reprocessing you must enter at the time of destruction or reprocessing the following particulars in the relevant section of the record:

- the total volume of spoilt wine destroyed
- the strength of the spoilt wine destroyed
- the date, time, place, and method of destruction
- the volume and strength of the wine in each container from which the spoilt wine was directly destroyed
- the amount of duty charged or paid and the amount of spoilt wine relief claimed
- the description of the wine returned by each purchaser in respect of which a claim is made
- the name and address of each purchaser, and
- the numbers and sizes of each container in which the wine was returned by each purchaser.

At the end of the accounting period, total the entries in your spoilt wine record of all wine destroyed or reprocessed and transfer the total to your wine duty account. When you submit your next monthly return, deduct the duty you are reclaiming by entering it on the reverse of the EX606 as appropriate. If HMRC is not satisfied with your explanation and supporting evidence, it will require you to repay the duty you claimed.

Trade samples

You may take samples for genuine wholesale or retail trade customers provided you enter the quantities and reasons for removal in your samples records. Trade samples must not be intended for public consumption, must not exceed one litre per product, and must be clearly labelled 'NOT FOR SALE'. There must be a genuine trade purpose for supplying the samples, for example, for analysis and tests before purchase. If samples are not supplied free of charge then you must pay duty on them.

Wine used for promotions and for tasting at, for example, trade fairs, shows, exhibitions and supermarkets must be duty-paid.

Domestic consumption

If you are a grower or beekeeper who produces or has produced for you wine from your own fruit or honey, you may deliver from your premises duty-free approved quantities of wine for your own domestic consumption, or for drinking free of charge by employees and guests. The maximum quantity allowed in any calendar year is 5.5 hectolitres plus 10% of the quantity above 5.5hl produced in the preceding calendar year up to a maximum of 11hl. To claim this relief, you must record your domestic consumption calculation in your business records before you remove your entitlement. As long as no charge is made for admission to the premises, no charge is made for the wine, and the wine is supplied by the glass and not in bottles or other takeaway packaging, you may regard visitors as guests and the drink consumed may be taken from your domestic consumption allowance.

Vine leasing for domestic consumption

Vine leasing is when the owner of a vineyard leases a number of vines (or rows of vines) to an individual or group of individuals so they can receive the wine produced from the vines they lease.

Lessees can receive wine duty free provided it is for their own domestic use and there are no commercial considerations. You may be asked to produce contracts or agreements for inspection.

To be regarded as growers, lessees must take responsibility for all work on their vines. This need not be done personally: lessee growers may contract other to carry out the work for them, but are responsible for the supervision of any contracted work. Lessee growers may present only the grapes from their own vines for vinification and may only receive wine produced from their own grapes.

The vineyard owner must not attend to the cultivation, nurturing or harvesting of the leased vines unless separately contracted to do so by the lessee and may not supplement the harvest of leased vines from any other source. Lessee-growers must be permitted to take their grapes elsewhere for vinification. The vineyard owner must maintain records of each lessee and the quantity of grapes presented for vinification with relative dates and times. Although the vineyard owner may make into wine the grapes from more than one lessee at the same time, each lessee must receive only that proportion of wine which relates to his grapes. If any of these rules are not observed, the wine produced will be liable to duty.

Records and accounts

As a revenue trader, you must observe the requirements of Notice 206 Revenue traders' records. HMRC may examine:

- Profit and Loss and Trading Statements
- Management Accounts and Reports
- Internal and external auditor's reports, and

- Any record maintained for a business purpose.
- Under regulation 6 of the Revenue Trader (Accounts and Records) Regulations 1992 you must keep records which show:
- Materials used (including additives)
- Details of processes and operations including fermentations, additions, drawing off, and bottling and packaging
- Quantities and strength of wine produced, received, sent out from licensed premises, returned to licensed premises, constructively removed, lost or destroyed on licensed premises and rendered sparkling
- Trade samples
- Domestic consumption
- Imports and exports
- Receipts, and
- Details of stocktakes, including any surplus, deficiency or other discrepancy revealed by the stocktake.
- Generally your normal business records will contain or can be modified to contain the required information.
- You must also keep a duty account summarising the duty due in each accounting period containing the following information:
- the amount of duty on all wine that leaves duty suspension
- the amount of duty reclaimed on spoilt wine which has been destroyed or wine which has been reprocessed
- the amount of any underdeclarations and overdeclarations from previous periods, and
- the net amount of duty due for the period and the date, and method of payment.

You must normally keep your business records for six years. If, however, this causes problems ask the Excise & Customs Helpline, phone 0845 010 9000, if you can keep some of your records for a shorter period. You must get HMRC agreement before destroying any business records that are less than six years old.

You can keep your records on any form of storage technology provided that copies can be easily produced and that there are adequate facilities for allowing HMRC to view them when required. If you keep your records on computer, HMRC will require access to it may require help from you or anyone else having charge of, or otherwise concerned with, the operation of the computer or its software.

Measurement of quantity

HMRC can require duty to be accounted for on the actual quantity of wine in each container as it passes the duty point. However when accounting for quantities in small packs (ie 10 litres or less), most packagers use the 'average system' of quantity control. Under this arrangement the average contents of packages must not be less than the declared contents (that is, that marked on the can or bottle or label). Within specified limits the actual contents of any particular container may be more or less than the declared contents. Packagers using the average system conform to a Weights & Measures Code of Practice agreed with Trading Standards.

Packagers are obliged to monitor and record the actual quantity of wine by sampling a proportion of packages to make sure they fulfil the Code's requirement. You are required to take at least one sample of a minimum of five packages for each production run. The average of the samples will be treated as the quantity of wine in a container. You should monitor the filling process to make sure that the quantity put into the package does not regularly exceed the amount declared on the label. You should record these checks and provide an adequate audit trail. Where there is evidence of consistent excessive overfilling, additional duty will be due.

In accounting for quantities sold in containers in excess of 10 litres, the dutiable quantity should be the actual contents found by dipping, metering or weighing.

Movement of wine in duy suspension

All intra-UK movements of wine need to be submitted through the Excise Movement & Control System (EMCS) unless they qualify for the simplified procedure. An electronic administrative document (eAD) will have to be raised on EMCS before the movement can start. EMCS automatically allocates an Administrative Reference Code (ARC) that uniquely identifies the movement. The ARC will be on the printed copy of the eAD or should be noted on the commercial document and must travel with the goods. For further information on EMCS procedures, see Notice 197.

The simplified procedure applies to certain UK movements and allows wine, cider, and perry in duty suspension to be moved between Excise-licensed premises using commercial or Customs documentation instead of EMCS for blending, mixing with other ingredients, conditioning, bottling or kegging, rendering sparkling, or destruction. You will be responsible for the duty on the wine until you receive a receipt. The receiving producer must sign an acceptable wine duty receipt (for example, the delivery note). If you do not obtain a receipt within four months, you will be liable for the duty. If you subsequently receive a receipt, you may credit your duty account with the appropriate amount.

The procedure is limited to movements from one licensed producer to another within the same company; from a producer to a third-party processer or excise warehouse provided that ownership remains with the producer; and for direct export where the dispatching producer is authorised for Local Clearance Procedures (LCP) and can provide a full customs export declaration.

You may also remove wine without payment of duty to an Excise warehouse approved under Section 92 of the Customs & Excise Management Act 1979 for the following purposes:

- fortification

- export, shipment as stores, or removal to the Isle of Man
- use in the manufacture of goods allowed to be produced in an Excise warehouse
- bottling
- storage and subsequent delivery to home-use or another warehouse
- rendering sparkling.
- After any of the above, the wine may be returned to you.
- In the case of finished and packaged product, each package must carry a satisfactory identifying mark and number. Containers must be full, and each case must hold containers of uniform size.

If the movement is under EMCS, an eAD will have to be raised on EMCS before the movement can start.

Keep a copy of the despatch document and the warehouse keeper's receipt for your own records.

Your normal commercial despatch documents will be suitable if they contain all the following information:

- the name and address of your premises
- a unique reference number
- the name and address of the premises you are sending the wine to
- the date of despatch
- a description of the wine, including the quantity, and
- a statement indicating that the wine is being moved in duty suspension.

If you are reciving wine for any of the above processes, you must:

- inspect the delivery vehicle to make sure it is secure and locks and seals are intact
- examine all containers etc. externally for signs of damage
- check the delivery against the document accompanying the wine
- issue a receipt within five days of the wine being received. If movement under EMCS, this will be a report of receipt or, if under simplified procedures, a certificate of receipt (for example, copy of delivery note) signed by an authorised person
- *record issue of the receipt*
- *enter the quantity received into your stock records, and*
- *keep the accompanying document.*

If you discover a discrepancy between the wine received and the accompanying document, you must issue a receipt only for the wine you actually receive. Show the discrepancy clearly on the certificate of receipt or include an inventory of the shortage or loss in the report of receipt.The wine received becomes part of your stock and is subject to the same rules as the product you produce on your licensed premises. For further details on procedures for inter-warehouse removals see Notice 197.

Index